Fossils, Paleontology and Evolution

Fossils, Paleontology and Evolution

BROWN FOUNDATIONS OF EARTH SCIENCE SERIES

David L. Clark
University of Wisconsin

WM. C. BROWN COMPANY PUBLISHERS
Dubuque, Iowa

FOUNDATIONS OF EARTH SCIENCE SERIES

Consulting Editor

DR. SHERWOOD D. TUTTLE
University of Iowa

Printed in the United States of America

Biology

FOSSILS, PALEONTOLOGY
AND EVOLUTION

David L. Clark
University of Wisconsin

History

HISTORICAL GEOLOGY OF
NORTH AMERICA

R. L. Langenheim, Jr.
University of Illinois

STRATIGRAPHY AND
GEOLOGIC TIME

John W. Harbaugh
Stanford University

Geography
Oceanography Geodesy Climatology
Cartography

GEOGRAPHY,
CLIMATOLOGY
AND OCEANOGRAPHY

George R. Rumney
University of Connecticut

BROWN
FOUNDATIONS
OF
EARTH
SCIENCE
SERIES

Quaternary Studies and Archeology

PLEISTOCENE GLACIATION
AND THE COMING OF MAN

W. N. Melhorn
Purdue University

Physical Geography and Hydrology

LANDFORMS AND
LANDSCAPES

Sherwood D. Tuttle
University of Iowa

Chemistry

EARTH MATERIALS

Henry Wenden
Ohio State University

Engineering and Mining

APPLIED EARTH SCIENCE

Daniel S. Turner
Eastern Michigan University

Physics

GEOPHYSICS, GEOLOGIC
STRUCTURES AND TECTONICS

John S. Sumner
University of Arizona

Astronomy

ASTRONOMY AND THE
ORIGIN OF THE EARTH

Theodore G. Mehlin
Williams College

Man is a creature of the earth. Second to knowledge of man himself is the necessity to understand the earth. The comprehensive study of the earth and its phenomena is termed earth science. The subject area intersects numerous college disciplines. To gain a thorough scientific understanding of the earth, one must study astronomy, meteorology, oceanography, geology and geophysics, plus aspects of geography and engineering. Additionally, comprehension of these topics requires a prior knowledge of such areas as mathematics, physics, chemistry and biology.

The knowledge explosion which has occurred during the twentieth century has made this approach impossible for the educated layman. Nevertheless, the need to understand our earth has become increasingly necessary.

The **FOUNDATIONS OF EARTH SCIENCE** Series, designed for use at the introductory level, incorporates into the scientific study of the earth an understanding of what components comprise the earth, their distribution, and an understanding of how and why they exist as they are, and how they affect civilized man.

Almost all of what we know about life in the geologic past has been developed from the study of fossils. **Fossils, Paleontology and Evolution,** in its discussions of biologic relationships, paleoecology and the complex nature of succeeding generations, deals with the intriguing subject of ancient life and helps us develop a history of life on earth.

Preface

This book is a survey of fossils, their study and what their interpretation means in the context of earth history. It is neither a fossil collectors guide nor a text for advanced paleontology. Hopefully, it will find use in both areas and serve as a guide for an introduction to life of the past for students of earth science.

Much of this material was absorbed from teachers, colleagues and students at six universities. Acknowledgment is due to the many people who have aided in my understanding of paleontology. Miss Dorothea Fuchs, Institut für Paläontologie, Bonn, adapted the drawings from many sources and Judy Meyer, University of Wisconsin, prepared the charts. Louise Boley Clark aided in many editorial matters.

David L. Clark

Acknowledgments

H. N. Andrews, Jr., *Studies in Paleobotany,* New York: John Wiley & Sons, Inc., 1961. Used with permission of author and publisher.

A. H. Cheetham, "Late Eocene Zoogeography of the Eastern Gulf Coast Region," *Geological Society of America Memoir 91,* 1963. Used with permission of author and The Geological Society of America.

E. H. Colbert, *Evolution of the Vertebrates,* New York: John Wiley & Sons, Inc., 1955. Used with permission of publisher.

William C. Darrah, *Principles of Paleobotany* 2nd ed., Copyright © 1960, The Ronald Press Company, New York.

Invertebrate Paleontology by William H. Easton. Copyright © 1960 by W. H. Easton. Reprinted by permission of Harper & Row, Publishers.

Invertebrate Fossels by R. C. Moore, C. G. Lalicker and A. G. Fischer. By permission of McGraw-Hill Book Company.

H. M. Muir-Wood, and G. A. Cooper, "Morphology, Classification and Life Habits of the Productoidea (Brachiopoda)," *Geological Society of America Memoir 81,* 1960. Used with permission of the authors and the Geological Society of America.

A. S. Romer, *Vertebrate Paleontology* 2nd ed., Chicago: The University of Chicago Press, 1950. Used with permission of author and publisher.

E. C. Stumm, "Silurian and Devonian Corals of the Falls of the Ohio," *Geological Society of America Memoir 93,* 1964. Used with permission of author and The Geological Society of America.

Treatise on Invertebrate Paleontology, courtesy of The Geological Society of America and The University of Kansas Press.

R. P. Wodehouse, *Pollen Grains,* New York: McGraw-Hill Book Company, 1959. Used with permission of publisher.

Contents

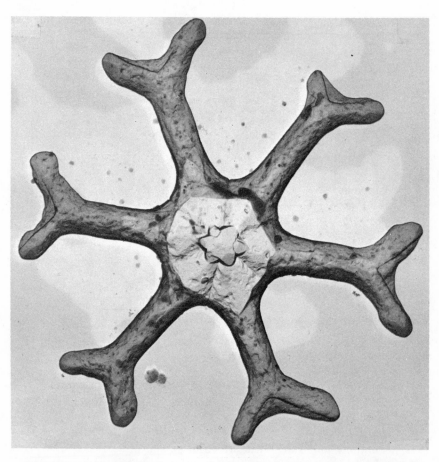

Discoaster challengeri Bramlette and Riedel. A microfossil from a deep sea core taken at a depth of 4975 meters in the mid-Atlantic, 13° 15′ North, 40° 40′ West. The fossil came from 1120 cm. below the top of the core and is here magnified 22,000 times in an electron microscope photograph (courtesy of Allan W. H. Bé).

Paleontology

The history of paleontology is one of observation and formulation of ideas and then developing theories. Theories have led to the recognition of facts which then have served as guidelines to procedures in paleontological research.

PHILOSOPHY OF PALEONTOLOGY

Paleontology is the study of ancient life, but today is not limited to the investigation of life in previous geologic periods. In a logical attempt to more fully interpret ancient life, the study of paleontology has been expanded to include a variety of living things. The modern paleontologist may be as much at ease on board ship taking samples of marine life from the North Atlantic as he is collecting 300 million year-old fossils from a mountain side in Nevada. In this modern pursuit, the study of paleontology may overlap that of zoology or botany. Such overlap is of little consequence, however, because both biology and paleontology are the study of life, and the time of its existence is simply becoming less a determining factor.

Those groups of fossils which are most fully understood are those having living relatives which can be observed and studied. It follows that the reason certain fossils are poorly understood is because there is no closely related living relative which has been identified. The dependency that fossil groups have with living types for adequate biological understanding has been recognized for a long time. This dependency was not always emphasized, however, and only recently have many students of paleontology concerned themselves with modern plants and animals.

Historically, most studies of fossils have been made in connection with applied work in which the utilization of fossils to determine the age of the rock in which they occur has been emphasized at the expense of their understanding as once-living organisms. In such studies, the identification and relative age of fossil groups have been stressed. This is very important and is still the first step in any systematic study, but we now realize that equally important for the interpretation of earth history is recognition that fossils are the remains or some indication of ancient forms of life. It is important to remember that fossils were once organisms which lived in environments with peculiar physical and chemical demands. They required specialized food for their physiologic processes and reproduced under particular conditions giving rise to new organisms which, with ancestors and descendants, participated in the continuing process of evolution.

HISTORY OF PALEONTOLOGY

As simple as such observations may appear today, it is interesting to note that man has not always understood fossils in this way. In past ages, men have believed many different things concerning fossils, and it has taken hundreds of years for our current ideas to develop. While the advances in the development of modern paleontologic philosophy are at least roughly correlated with the periods of mankind's intellectual development, the achievements of civilization in art, music and literature in times past, have far surpassed man's understanding of life, its origin and development through time.

Men were early concerned with the nature of fossils, but not from the viewpoint of how ancient life aided in the interpretation of earth history. The first problem was resolving the question: are fossils organic or inorganic? The Greeks were among the first to record their ideas on the nature of this problem. The names of Xenophanes, Herodotus, Aristotle and Theophrastus are prominent among early students, but in this early beginning of the observation of natural history, ideas were vague; references are perfunctory, and the sources for many references are questionable.

Evidently, Xenophanes and Herodotus visualized a relationship between fossil sea shells which were found on hillsides and ancient inundations of the land by the sea. Herodotus indicated that he, as well as most writers of this time, had little understanding of ancient life when he suggested that certain Eocene fossils found in Egypt were the remains of food left by the construction crews of the pyramids.

Concerned more with law, civil matters and architecture than with natural history, the Romans added little to man's study of ancient life.

Lucretius and the Plineys made observations during this period, and reference by these men and others to currently unknown writings by Greeks and other Romans suggest that more was known during these times than has been passed to the current generation.

During the late B.C. and early A.D. years, certain vague and mistaken ideas formed the principal philosophy of paleontology. But as small observations were added to meager data, some valid ideas developed and by the time of the Renaissance, men generally believed that fossils were organic in nature. Ideas concerning their origin were still primitive. Men debated whether fossils originated from the fermentation of slime and "fatty matter" in the earth, were the incomprehensible creations of the Creator, or were made by the Devil to deceive man. In Italy, Leonardo da Vinci, among others, stressed the natural and organic origin and nature of fossils and in the middle of the seventeenth century, Nicolaus Steno of Denmark published his views that molluscs and fossil teeth from "lumps of earth" in Malta were the remains of marine animals and that the part of the earth around Malta must, at one time, have been covered by water.

As the fact that fossils were organic in nature and natural by origin became acceptable, different theses were advanced to explain fossils observed distribution on the mountains and hills, places long held to be immutable. During the eighteenth century the Biblical flood of Noah's time was credited with the mass mortality supposedly evidenced by the fossils of the earth. Because this was in apparent agreement with religious views theological leaders gave this idea powerful support for many years, and although this view acknowledged an organic nature and origin for fossils, because of its catastrophic implications, it did not lead to a systematic philosophy of paleontology.

Paleontology became a science at the beginning of the nineteenth century. Cuvier and Lamarck in France and Smith in England began to lay the foundation of observation which lifted the study of fossils from the doldrums of superstition to a ranking position among the natural sciences. It became apparent to Cuvier, a professor in the College de France in the early 1800's, that the fossil mammals which he pieced together bone by bone were not dead representatives of living species but extinct types and in many cases, ancestral to living forms. He also noted that fossils in different layers of the earth were generally different and that this must be an indication that they were of different ages. His ideas on one mass destruction following another to explain extinction of different forms of life are not considered valid today. At approximately the same time, Lamarck, a Professor of Zoology at the Natural History Museum in Paris, began to accumulate a vast amount of data on invertebrate fossils. His study of the animals without backbones lead to the famous theory of organic evolution. Lamarck believed that acquired characteristics could be inherited by another generation of organisms and that change of characteristics through time was very much dependent on the environment. This was one of the first serious attempts at a synthesis of ideas on origin, nature and distribution of life. Although modified in scope, some of Lamarck's ideas are still considered part of the working hypothesis of organic evolution.

Of equal importance in the elevation of paleontology to a first class science was the work of William Smith in England. Smith, who worked on various engineering and surveying teams in extremely fossiliferous strata in England, began to note that certain types of fossils were always associated with specific rock layers. More observations confirmed this and he published several volumes describing his finds plus the first geologic map of England. In almost every kind of human endeavor, at least early in its history, there must be some practical justification for study, a justification which serves as the catalyst to get other people interested. As more people become interested, more work is done and then knowledge increases quickly. Smith demonstrated that fossils were useful and had definite value for recognition and definition of the layers of the earth. He was able to show that rock layers separated geographically could be correlated by their contained fossils. Thus, stratigraphic paleontology or biostratigraphy was born. Since this time, the utilization of fossils in the interpretation of rock strata has been a primary motivation for their study.

After Smith, paleontology had a purpose in addition to study for study's sake. Then in 1859, Darwin published his ideas on organic evolution and it was recognized that fossils were the evidence for this theory. Sequences of fossils from different layers of the earth were then studied with ancestors and descendants in mind and when such relationships were determined some of the tempo and a bit of the mode of evolution for the first time became known. The reasons for the distribution of fossils and living organisms in time and space could now be explained quite logically.

The study of fossils has branched in many directions during the last hundred years. The value of fossils in the interpretation of age and relationships of the rock layers of the earth is universally recognized and studies related to this are still among the most important. Many of the principal lineages or phylogenies have been determined and with the help of Darwin's theory and an understanding of modern genetics, details of the "how" of evolution through millions of years of earth history are becoming clear. Still, there are many undescribed or "new" species of animals and plants which are yearly culled from the rocks of the earth. And with each new find, the paleontologist who prepares a careful description of his discovery adds another page to the book of the life and history of the earth.

Paleontological research moves through a series of steps designed to give additional knowledge. The descriptive stage is first and then the determination of a fossil's position in time (biostratigraphy) and space (paleozoogeography). Finally, the relationship of a fossil and the group or population to which it belongs, as well as its contemporary life and the dependency between the organism and the chemical and physical factors of its former environment must be determined (paleo-ecology).

So, the study of paleontology, initiated in the midst of ignorance of natural processes and nurtured by medieval superstition, has emerged in the twentieth century as the champion of evolutionary theory and as a skeleton key to the interpretation of the rocks of the earth.

2

Fossils

Fossils or the indication of life of a previous geologic period are preserved through diverse processes. Agents working against fossilization probably have destroyed more potential fossils than have been preserved.

DEFINITIONS

The word fossil comes from a Latin word meaning "dug from the earth" and in its original usage, "fossil" was applied to rocks and minerals, as well as to organic remains. When it became apparent that rocks, minerals, and "fossils" were different in origin and nature, the word fossil was reserved for *the remains or indication of the remains of life of previous geologic periods.*

Perhaps the biggest wonder is how ancient life could be preserved at all; for everywhere life vanishes at death, leaves fall and decompose, animals die and are destroyed by bacterial action. And this is apparently the way that it has always been, so the preservation or fossilization of any form of life is somewhat remarkable.

FOSSILIZATION

The requirements for preservation of a fossil are rigorous. For one thing, an organism should have some part which is capable of being preserved and this prerequisite eliminates great numbers of soft bodied animals and plants. Bones or a hard shell are among the most effectively preserved materials and the majority of fossils are of this type (Fig. 1). With the exception of certain mammals of the recent ice age,

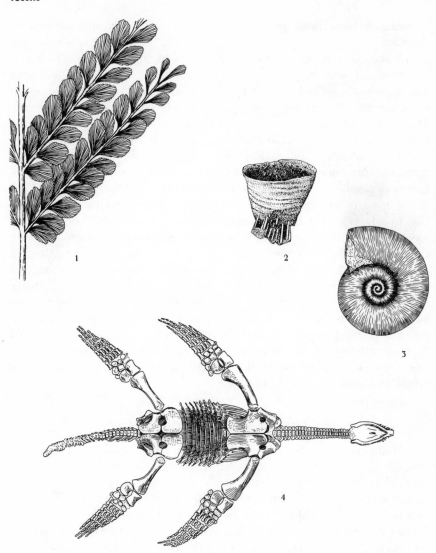

Figure 1. Types of fossils. 1. **Archaeopteris hibernica,** an Upper Devonian plant a few inches in length; 2. and 3. invertebrates, **2. Prorichthofenia permiana,** an unusual Permian brachiopod, X 2; 3. **Metalytoceras triboleti,** a Cretaceous cephalopod; 4. **Thaumatosaurus,** a Jurassic plesiosaur, a vertebrate fossil approximately 11 feet long. Invertebrates and vertebrates are generally the best kinds of fossils because they had hard parts capable of being preserved and many lived in an environment (marine water) where sediment burial helped protect the hard parts. (1. adapted from Andrews; 2. after Muir-Wood and Cooper; 3. after Arkell et al.; 4. after Romer.)

no animals have been preserved with complete soft and hard parts together.

A second requirement is that the parts of the organism which can be preserved must be protected after death and a covering of sediment was apparently an aid to most fossils. Occasionally, under very unusual environmental conditions, impressions of soft parts may be preserved. These cases of preservations are rare but because of those which are known, our knowledge of life of the past has been greatly enhanced.

So, *capability* of an organism for preservation would seem to depend upon the presence of preservable parts and the *possibility* of preservation depends upon the protection of these parts through some kind of covering or an equally effective process. These conditions are satisfied to a large extent in the shallower parts of large water bodies which have abundant life and regularly receive some kind of sediment. Because these same conditions were widespread, especially in the continental seas of the past, most of the fossils known are marine invertebrates and vertebrates. Bones of large land vertebrates, the dinosaurs and mammals, are also preserved, but generally only when the bones were associated with lakes or streams where a supply of sediment could entomb them. Fossil birds and the remains of arboreal organisms or types which would not generally be associated with water are very rare. Most fossil plant material is preserved in aquatic sediment which seems to indicate proximity to water.

CHANGE AND PRESERVATION

If the prerequisites for preservation are met, how is an organism actually preserved? Some parts of organisms are preserved in their original condition, that is, bone or shell material may be preserved as in the condition of life with little or no chemical alteration. Teeth are especially durable objects and fossil teeth are among the most useful fossils. Indeed, the study of fossil mammals may have been considerably less successful if it were not for the preservation of teeth which are so important for mammal interpretation.

An instant deep freeze provided by the last ice age caught and froze some mammals and preserved them much the same way a fish may be preserved in a home freezer. These are the ideal fossils, because flesh, internal organs, as well as bone and skin are preserved. Unfortunately, during only the last few thousand years of earth history have these conditions provided us with fossils. Mummification by preservation in oil and peat bogs or in unusually dry cave conditions is another method of preservation, but like the ice, this type of preservation only worked effectively for present research during the last few thousand years of geologic time.

Many marine invertebrates such as clams, corals, sponges and sea urchins have a hard shell or skeletal structure, parts of which may be preserved. Calcium carbonate ($CaCO_3$) is a common shell or skeletal material and is readily preserved, often in an unaltered condition. Hard parts may be replaced with solutions rich in iron, silica or other carbonate material, altering an original structure with a molecule by molecule substitution. Commonly a fossil may not be replaced, but is dissolved by circulating ground water and only an impression of the fossil is left. Such a void or mold may serve to identify the former fossil or the cavity may be filled by another mineral deposited from solution. In this way, casts (replicas of the original shell), may result.

Often an incompletely understood distillation process may preserve the carbonized remains of delicate tissue of an animal or a leaf. Some of the most useful fossils are carbon impressions of ancient marine life.

Fossils may be simply the evidence of life such as trails or tracks. Excrement left by living things has even been preserved and is useful in determining a fossil's former eating habits.

ORGANIC CONSTITUENTS

Shells and other structures which are not greatly altered after the time of their burial may preserve some of their original organic constituents. Amino-acids have been identified in fossil material 2000 million years old and fatty-acids in amounts of 2×10^{-4} to 10^{-5} are known to exist in ancient sediment. The fact that these organic constituents, long thought incapable of being preserved, have recently been identified in rock, has given new insight into the manner of preservation.

TIME AND FOSSILS

The passage of time works against fossil preservation. Different conditions of environment have existed and each change has possessed the capabilities of destroying a previously well preserved fauna. Uplift of parts of the earth and the exposure of rocks to the forces of weathering and erosion, or ground water and the elevated temperatures associated with volcanic activity, are only a few of the geological processes which have been operating for five billion years of earth history. Most of the history of life has been learned from rocks less than 600 million years old, and the uncertainty associated with fossils which have been described from older rocks is amplified by the continual destructive work of geological processes. In spite of the rigorous requirements for preservation and the abrading effect of geologic processes, numerous fossils have been preserved and the history of life of the past is becoming well understood.

CHAPTER

3

Evolution

Although fossils have been reported from rocks two to three billion years old, they are abundant only in rocks 600 million years or less in age. The origin of life is inextricably woven in the fabric of the early atmosphere and hydrosphere. The evolution of all three must be understood in terms of their relationship. Evolution of life and its genetical mechanism is well documented and understood on different levels.

OLDEST LIFE

Fossils are not common in rocks which are more than 600 million years old. One might assume from this fact that life on the earth was not very abundant prior to this date. The evidence at hand would largely confirm such an assumption. In recent years, however, a surprising number of fossils have been found in rocks which for many years were thought to have been formed before life itself. Precambrian fossils (pre-600 million years) are now known from every continent except Antarctica and although the exact age relationship of these interesting fossil discoveries is not adequately understood, their discovery indicates that life has been on earth for at least two or even three billion years.

Only a few of the fossils in these Precambrian rocks definitely can be identified or compared with types which are living today. Those that are not much older than 600 million years are the most familiar. Fossils of this age identified in Canada and Australia are not as peculiar as the microorganisms which are known to occur elsewhere in Canada and South Africa and which are much older. These microorganisms are extremely abundant in certain layers on two continents but their identification and classification are hindered by their extremely small size. Nonetheless, their occurrence gives us a point in history some three billion years ago when life was already present on earth.

With such a point in time for a start, it becomes interesting to trace the development of life in its many forms.

ORIGIN OF LIFE

The problem of the origin of life on earth is one to which almost every field of science from paleontology to astrophysics and from nuclear chemistry to paleoclimatology has contributed. Because the origin of life is a subject which deals with so many factors, many approaches to the problem are possible.

For instance, what conditions are necessary for the formation of life? If these conditions are different from those on earth today, what evidence is there that they ever existed? Did these things exist in a time sequence which is coherent with a life origin theory?

Among the most important prerequisites for the formation of life on earth are the following:

    a. ammonia, hydrogen, nitrogen, water, and possibly methane and carbon dioxide,

    b. a source of energy,

    c. a reducing (oxygen free) atmosphere (Table 1).

In the laboratory, the synthesis of complex organic molecules from materials such as listed above and under these conditions is possible. A number of techniques using slightly different materials and methods have been demonstrated for more than 20 years. Very simply, combinations of hydrogen, carbon, methane, nitrogen — all inorganic — in a water environment devoid of any free oxygen can be stimulated to form complex "organic" molecules when exposed to certain doses of radiation. There are several schools of thought on the exact composition of the material involved and on the source of energy possible. Theories differ because of different physical chemical or bio-chemical backgrounds (Table 1). Nonetheless, because the production of organic molecules, which are the basic building blocks of living matter, can be obtained from an inorganic system in the laboratory; the second question is whether these conditions ever existed naturally on earth?

The answer to this important question seems to be positive on all counts. For instance:

TABLE 1

Composition of the primitive atmosphere

A*	B*
CH_4	CO_2
NH_3	CO
H_2	H_2
H_2O vapor	N_2
	H_2O vapor

*from Rasool, S. I., 1967, Evolution of the Earth's Atmosphere: Science, v. 157, p. 1466-1467; according to Rasool, A corresponds to atmospheric composition proposed by Oparin, Miller, Urey and Ponnamperuma; B that proposed by Abelson and others.

1. Most of the best theories for the origin of earth include ideas which demand the presence of the very things which the biochemists say would have been necessary for the origin of life. The evidence is based on calculations of the primary chemical constituents of the earth as well as upon present astronomical observations on the abundance of elements in our solar system. All of these observations seem to indicate that the H_2, N_2, H_2O, and other chemical items are precisely the compounds which would be present in any primitive atmosphere of a planet such as the earth.

2. Also, the energy source, whether high energy ultraviolet radiation or a spark of lightning, also would have been available. Recent data from artificial satellites indicates the presence above the earth's surface of various layers of radiation "belts" which must have evolved with our earth. The absence of these shields early in the earth's history would have allowed a much greater amount of high energy radiation to come to earth than can currently pass through the atmosphere. Here is one radiation source which was probably of sufficient magnitude for the actions and reactions proposed for the origin of life.

3. The third of the three prerequisites for the origin of life is the presence of an oxygen free or as it is called chemically, a reducing atmosphere. The demonstration of such a condition three to four billion years ago would appear at first glance to be difficult, but

geochemists, biologists and paleoclimatologists have gathered unique data related to this point. First, it is interesting to note that the best theories for the origin of the earth indicate that oxygen is one of the elements which could not have existed in a free condition when the earth was formed. Free oxygen was evidently limited to 0.1 percent of the present atmospheric level in the beginning. Further, the presence of oxygen in today's atmosphere is almost completely biologically produced and therefore must have been essentially absent before there was life on the earth. These biologically deduced facts are profound but perhaps of equal importance is the record of the sediment which paleoclimatologists and geochemists have interpreted. This record is concerned with "oxidized sediment" or, more particularly, iron-rich sediment which has been exposed to the atmosphere. Oxidation or rusting is, of course, common today and most things in our present atmosphere are attacked by oxygen. Oxidized sediment is unknown in the rock record prior to one billion years ago. The appearance of numerous oxidized sediment or "red beds" in the geologic record evidently coincides with the abundance of oxygen-producing organisms. Before this time, neither the oxygen nor the organisms which could produce it were present. These observations suggest again, that when the earth was very young, a reducing atmosphere was present.

Substantiation of the actual presence of the material, energy and environment for production of life is only the first step. More difficult to substantiate are the ideas on the steps between the formation of life's building blocks and their development into the complex molecules which gave rise to living things. This has been referred to as molecular ordering and while actual life production in the laboratory may be a few years away, this molecular ordering does not seem impossible. Biochemists have demonstrated that inherent electrical charges on molecules may cause alignment and organization of matter into biologic systems. These steps also have been demonstrated under controlled laboratory conditions which, in turn, can be related to definite facts concerning conditions of the early earth. All of these factors point to the primeval sea as the setting for the origin of life.

In this primitive and quite sterile environment, the transformation of inorganic compounds into organic structures and then molecular ordination proceeded. It was a slow development but in an environment devoid of free oxygen and life forms which might devour them, primitive life-like cells began to form. It has been estimated that up to one percent concentration of organic material in the sea may have been produced in this way. Time and change and more transformation, and primitive life formed. All of the essentials were present and all of the time needed for the slow process was available.

These ideas, theories and occasional facts give a coherent, if less than completely satisfactory idea on the origin of life. Significant in all observations is the fact that many different scientific disciplines have added a fact here, an idea there, and that there is general agreement. Such consistency could be regarded as an indication of the validity of the idea.

A final important consideration is the time factor. Assuming that all of the conditions demonstrated to be necessary for the formation of life were indeed present, what information is there on the contemporaneity of their presence? Here paleontological evidence and physical dating have given a point in time when such events did occur. We know from our study of the sedimentary record that oxidized sediment, which must have formed in an oxidizing atmosphere, began forming approximately one billion years ago. Also, limestones thought to be related to biologic activity did not form prior to two billion years ago. Life was clearly present and perhaps more abundant than the fossil record has yet revealed at this early time. Primitive life types similar to fungi and blue-green algae living today are present in considerable abundance in Precambrian rocks which have been dated as two billion years old in Canada. Similar types which are three billion years old have been found in South Africa. The exact nature of the two to three billion year old fossils is difficult to understand because the small sphere and rod-like types are not exactly like any living thing. The presence of this early life in two to three billion year old sediment suggests that it may have been the dominant life-type for a billion or more years. No evidence of any oxidizing atmosphere before this time has been found and the conditions of a young earth, only a billion or so years removed from its formation, seem to furnish the other prerequisites and all in the necessary sequence.

From the earliest forms of life, more sophisticated types with more efficient functions evolved. A remarkable assemblage of many different fossils is now known in Australia from rocks of late Precambrian age, perhaps less than one billion years old. These fossils include worm-like, coral-like, and sponge-like forms, plus types not similar to any marine invertebrate of today's oceans. This discovery seems to confirm diversity of life only two billion years removed from the earliest types known.

Early forms of life prospered, reproduced, diversified, adapted, and many kinds became extinct. The more successful forms left descendants who, in turn, found their niche on earth, reproduced their kind, and life continued. The slow pattern of change is distinct.

The processes involved in change through time are only today being described in the detail necessary for full comprehension, but the fundamental pattern and scope of organic change was first described more than 100 years ago by Charles Darwin. From the origin of life, our observations must now move to its evolution.

EVOLUTION OF LIFE

The Record of Change

Darwin was not the first naturalist to have insight into the process of evolution but his geological background and biological interests endowed him with better equipment with which to build a theory of organic evolution than any of his predecessors. Darwin pointed out that the interaction of a changing environment and a changeable organism would produce varied life forms, each of which was limited by biological make-up to a relatively narrow environmental niche. Change in structure was slow and although the ability for change of any structure came from "within" the successfulness of any change was related to externally produced conditions. The study of genetics and biochemistry has provided the explanation of the change which comes from "within" and the working of the gene. The study of the structure of the chromosome, deoxyribonucleic acid (DNA) and how mutations may occur, are all part of many secondary school curricula. But what bearing do all of these things have on the evolution of life? What is the mechanism which has been in operation and which is responsible for the change from the simple life forms of the Precambrian to the more complex types of the Cambrian and of the Recent? (Fig. 2)

Our first observation should be concerned with the record of life which has been preserved in the rocks of the earth. From the oldest rocks to the youngest, each section contains different types of fossils. Many types were completely unique to their time interval, unlike types in older or younger rock layers. It is also clear that some fossil types represent races which lived for millions of years with very little change.

For instance, certain brachiopods of the Ordovician Period had shells which were very similar to shells of types living today. While there may have been differences in the soft parts, the shelled part changed very little during 400 million years. In contrast, certain cephalopods, which are relatives of the modern squid and octopus, changed so rapidly that a single species lived unchanged for a very short period of time — perhaps less than 800,000 years. Almost all groups of animals,

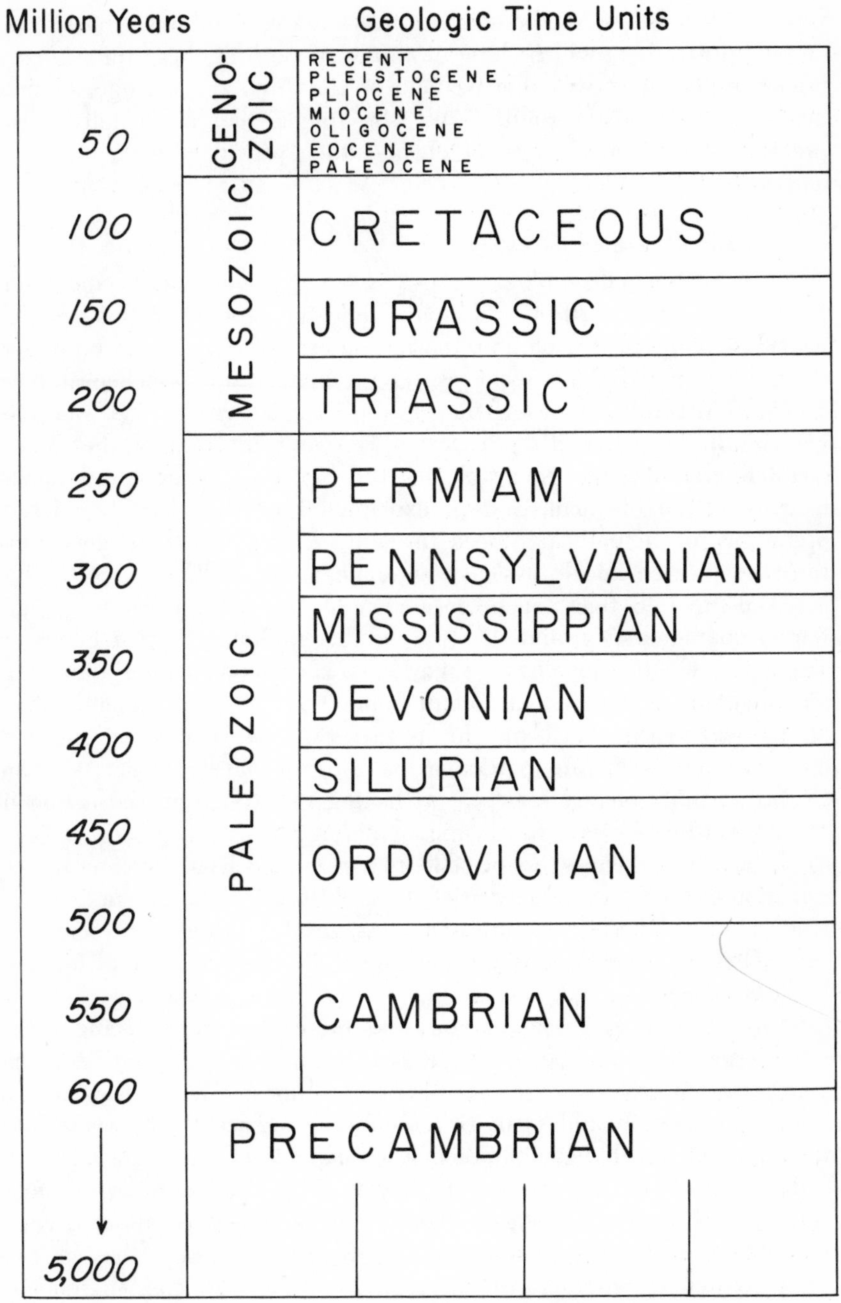

Million Years   Geologic Time Units

Million Years		
50	CENO-ZOIC	RECENT PLEISTOCENE PLIOCENE MIOCENE OLIGOCENE EOCENE PALEOCENE
100	MESOZOIC	CRETACEOUS
150		JURASSIC
200		TRIASSIC
250	PALEOZOIC	PERMIAM
300		PENNSYLVANIAN
350		MISSISSIPPIAN
		DEVONIAN
400		SILURIAN
450		ORDOVICIAN
500		
550		CAMBRIAN
600		
↓		PRECAMBRIAN
5,000		

Figure 2.   Geologic Time Scale. (Dates modified from Kulp.)

vertebrates (with a backbone) and invertebrates (without a backbone) have had members which show examples of both of these things. Most organisms changed with the passage of time and this change, or evolution, is well documented. While the fossils may never tell us the precise chemical mechanism of change, they provide the record of its occurrence.

Genetics and the Reason for Change

One of the paleontologist's tasks is the discovery, study and interpretation of the record of evolution. While the product of this research provides the facts of evolution, the mechanism of change can be understood best from living organisms. The geneticist and biochemist have given us much information during the last 50 years. The study of genetics has provided the answer to Darwin's problem of the factors "within" which were responsible for the biologic change in characteristics, and the biochemists have explained how the characteristics of organisms are actually produced through the joint action of genes and their complex chemical-physical environment.

We are told that a gene is a complex chemical package of "potential characteristics" and that the number of limbs, size of bones, or shape of shell that an organism may have is dependent upon the action and reaction of a particular set of genes with its environment. Genes are present in every cell and during growth, genes may relay chemical messages and stimulate particular patterns of development. We can, therefore, think of any structure as having resulted from the action of one or more genes with its chemical environment.

The genes themselves, present in the germ cell at the time of fertilization, are of tremendous variety, and different environmental stimuli may cause them to relay different messages for different responses in cells. One of the reasons there may be a great number of differences between ancestors and descendants is that there are a large number of genes in any given population, and in sexually reproducing populations, the large number of genes is constantly being reshuffled. One geneticist has pointed out that there are thousands of genes in the human population and from this number of genes there are tens of thousands of possible combinations, each capable of imparting a slightly different characteristic to the recipient. With this number of combinations, the variety of types, even in the human population, may be thought of as surprisingly few. This seems to be related to the fact that in a particular environment there are only a few combinations of characteristics which are really adaptable and while two heads and unchambered hearts and various other kinds of characteristics are possible and appear each year, only a single broad type does survive in our human environment. Any population, whether of clams or elephants, is now visualized as possessing a gene pool from which all of the characteristics of a population — advantageous and harmful — are actually drawn.

This variety of characteristics is hardly important when compared with the fact of change or mutation of genes. The fact that a gene may be chemically or physically altered and become a new characteristic potential adds new variety to life. Such changes or mutations occur for a variety of reasons, but they do occur, and this change is a continuing process. Because most populations are more or less adjusted to their environments, the majority of gene changes must be considered non-advantageous. For instance, an arbitrary change in the mechanism of a clock or some complicated piece of machinery is unlikely to improve its performance. Therefore, because gene mutations are random, they are also usually not advantageous to the organism. Gene changes occur, however, and this mutation is the source of the evolutionary process. The rate at which mutation occurs must differ in different organisms and may be increased by chemical or physical means. Also, there appear to have been times when evolution occurred much more rapidly than at other times. Many investigators have noticed that the greatest diversification of a group of organisms occurred soon after their initial appearance. Other students have related these times of widespread and rapid evolution to changes in the earth's atmosphere as it journeys through space. Time seems to be the important element in evolution. For during the billions of years of earth history, no external environment has remained the same for great lengths of time. The story of the earth, as well as that of life, is one of change. Where mountains are today, there once was a sea, deserts of the past are now covered by ice, and volcanic ash now covers areas which once were green with lush vegetation.

Each of these environmental changes, and there have been several billion years of them, has challenged the organisms which are dependent upon the temperature, food supply and the thousand other physical, chemical and biological factors which comprise an environment. Except for man, a change in an organism's environment has meant there must be some change in habit, structure, or function. Evolution takes place on the group level, not on the individual level. Whether or not a group adapts to a change is evidently dependent on whether or not there is present in the group population a form or forms which are capable of adaptation. The ability to adapt must be related to a characteristic or series of characteristics which the particular organism possesses. The appearance of such adaptiveness is related to the possible variants which have been introduced by a mutation of genes. If, in any population challenged by an environmental change, there is present a variant which can adapt for any reason, then that population, through the spread of the advantageous character, may become adaptive and the population may survive. In one way of speaking, that population will survive which has the greatest number of useful variants — present and potential. This fact is related, in part, to the number of offspring which are reproduced. There is, however, apparently an optimum population size in which advantageous characteristics can arise and spread. Reproduction rate alone was evidently no assurance of the ultimate success or survival for life in the past.

The Mechanism of Change

Visualize, for a general idea of evolution, an environment which is undergoing slow change. This change may take a million or more years to be completed. The rocks of the earth are a strong testimony to the fact of such change. Visualize a population of organisms in this environment, a population which is more or less adapted to the conditions at some point in time. With this working base, the stage is set for evolution — or extinction! What happens? Certain of the organisms may migrate geographically to areas where "pre-change" conditions can be found, or there may be a group which consists of members which can harmonize with the changing environment. Many environmental changes were slow but when they were too rapid, mass mortality resulted.

Whether the challenge thus posed by an environmental modification will cause mass mortality, migration, or encourage adaptation, is dependent upon the populations' "change potential" or gene pool. With the daily reshuffling of genes in most populations and the mutations of others, some variant, independent of the reason for the environmental change but advantageous because of it, may appear. If it does, the advantage imparted to that organism in the face of the environmental challenge, though small, may be significant. If the advantageous characteristic is disseminated, those individuals properly endowed may be the favored generation. Time and change and time and reproduction — and a new but advantageous characteristic may become common.

The record of life is not only one of evolution but also of extinction. Millions of species of animals and plants have lived and then, unable to adapt to some change in their environment, have become extinct. The familiar stories of the passenger pigeon, the whooping crane, the American buffalo (almost), the rhinoceros (soon), are those of the alternate to evolution — extinction! The fact of evolution itself involves extinction of a different sort because the very success of adaption has usually led to new generations whose structure ultimately separates them from their ancestors which then are extinct types.

Levels of Evolution

Evolution can be understood on many levels, the most important of which is the population or species level in which one species gives rise to another. Evolution may also be understood on the group level where characteristics of many families of larger groups experience modifications through time.

Species Level

During the Late Cambrian, certain marine animals contained minute calcium phosphate structures called conodonts. These conodont elements were, in general, quite rapidly evolving structures in response to some environmental pressure not yet understood. One evolutionary sequence has been studied in approximately 250 feet of rock in the Great Basin of western Utah. The time interval of this sequence can only be guessed at presently, but from comparisons with known radio-actively dated parts of the Cambrian, it would appear that one to two million years is represented in this 250 feet. At the base of this rock sequence a simple cone shaped conodont occurs in great numbers (Fig. 3). It is smooth sided and has a deep basal cavity and the structure is much like a hollow cone. Some 45 feet higher in the rock sequence, change has occurred and the thickness between the outer surface and the inner cavity is considerably greater. How many mutations this represents is of course unknown but something in the environment may have favored a thicker "skin." Another 30 feet higher in the section are great numbers of this same species but with a greatly reduced basal cavity and the thickened inner wall shows irregularities which are differentiated into a series of small bumps. At 100 feet above the occurrence of the original type, the differentiation of bumps is carried to a maximum and one or two of these develops into a secondary projection of definite magnitude. At this point, the differences between the original and ancestral generation are so marked that the new form is actually a different type. Evolution is a continuing process and 50 feet higher and thousands of years later the secondary projections are developed into three to five definite points directed laterally to the original cone. Expansion of the projections and reduction of the basal cavity continue in this species and another 100 feet higher (and another million years later), the lateral projections are seven or more in number, as high and prominent as the primitive cone and the

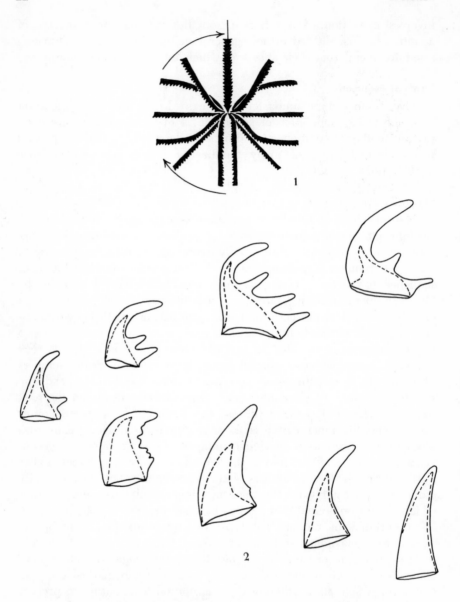

Figure 3.   Levels of evolution. 1. Group level shown by graptolite colonies. Earliest colonies had many branches which hung down but descendants had fewer branches which had reversed the direction of growth. Approximately one hundred million years are represented by this sequence; 2. Species level evolution demonstrated by conodonts in a 250 foot vertical section of Upper Cambrian-Lower Ordovician rocks, X100 (1. after Moore, Lalicker and Fischer.)

entire structure is more or less solid with the basal cavity now reduced to a small hollow area beneath the main cone. This stage in evolution is so distinct from the previous one that it is considered a different species. Thus three species with an ancestral-descendant relationship can be traced in 250 feet of rock representing one to two million years. What the environmental challenge was for this species is unknown but the change recorded is a good example of evolution at the population or species level.

GROUP LEVEL

Equally good examples are known on different levels. Another Paleozoic group of marine animals were the graptolites. These colonial animals consist of a central branch which forms the framework for numerous little compartments, each of which was probably occupied by a separate individual. During the Late Cambrian, 40 or more of these branches were present in a single colony. Some of the colonies were attached to the ocean floor but others may have floated in the water. By the Silurian time, progressive evolution had effectively modified the structure of similar colonies and only a single branch, which also had reversed its direction of growth, resulted. The intervening steps are also known, and reduction from 40 branches to one branch with reversal in relative direction of growth can be seen almost step by step. In this group, however, successive species change has not been determined with precision but these basic trends in evolution are well documented on the group level (Fig. 3).

Every group of organisms which has left a credible record in the rocks of the earth demonstrates evolution on some level. Although most groups have had successful members, even the most rapidly evolving groups have not always met the challenge throughout time. Both the conodonts and graptolites have been extinct for many million years.

4

Areas of Study in Paleontology

Paleontology is the study of life of the past. Although description and evolutionary studies are still of primary importance, exacting new tools have enabled the paleontologist to interpret paleoclimates as well as more specific areas of paleoecology.

The utilizations of fossils in the interpretation of earth history are diverse. One recent study was concerned with the fantastic chase of a squid-like fossil (cephalopod) by a pursuing swimming reptile more than 100 million years ago. Only the fossil shell has been found but its study shows that the reptile was able to sink its teeth into the shell of the cephalopod *sixteen* different times during the chase. From the study of the tooth points, the investigators were able to tell the direction and effectiveness of the various bites as well as the identity of the species of swimming reptile which was doing the biting. Supplementary to all of this was the observation of the diet of the swimming reptile. Evidently, the cephalopod was a good match for the reptile, at least for awhile, and the overlap of the toothprints on the cephalopod shell were interpreted in their chronologic order until a final and sixteenth bite ended the chase. This final bite severed the entire body chamber with all of the vital soft parts.

Of equal but different interest is a recent study which utilizes the known world distribution of numbers of fossils of a particular kind in a check on the ancient position of the earth's magnetic poles. This study, based on the fact that in modern oceans the number of varieties of most animals changes from a maximum at the equators to a minimum at the poles, enabled the investigator to determine if the paleontologic evidence favored or opposed so called polar wandering which has been suggested for past periods of geologic time.

Paleontologic studies seem coherent with the idea that fossils are the remains of life and that the interpretation of a fossil from the view of the time and environment in which it lived and died is important.

SYSTEMATIC PALEONTOLOGY

The oldest area of study in paleontology and perhaps still the most important, is the description and classification of fossils. Fossils must first be identified and the relationship that one fossil has with descendants and ancestors also must be considered and described. While this description now involves new techniques, the final product of systematic paleontology is as it has been for more than 100 years — the complete identification and classification of every fossil species. Such identifications usually rest in the hands of a specialist but some facility is acquired by most students of paleontology. This first step in the study of fossils will never be complete until all organisms that have lived are known. It has been estimated that 500,000,000 species of animals have lived. Approximately 1,130,000 species, living and fossil have been described.

The tools of the systematic paleontologist traditionally have been various cleaning implements to prepare fossil specimens as well as a pair of calipers to measure morphologic dimensions, and a reference library to aid in determining the relationships of the fossil at hand with those already described. These relationships are determined on the basis of morphologic similarity and often the comparison of features of anatomy and ornamentation has been subjective. The recent development of equipment which is very sensitive, quantitative and highly reliable in the measurement of very small quantities of preserved organic constituents shows great promise for systematic and evolutionary work. It is known that protein in shell and bone may be preserved for millions of years in an unaltered condition. Older material may still retain some of the initial structure of the amino acid, and free amino acids may be recognized in specimens more than a billion years old. Of considerable significance is the fact that the types and quantities of such organic constituents as amino acids present in a fossil are genetically controlled. Because similar animals have similar genetic structure, it may be possible to recognize genetic similarity through amino acid similarity.

More than 20 amino acids have been described in rocks up to a billion or more years old. Exactly what amino acid relationships may exist among the various groups of fossils is now beginning to be realized. If similarities in pattern between closely related fossil types can be proved, the systematic paleontologist may have a new and exacting tool for aid in determination of relationships. Fatty acids and other organic constituents may be preserved in fossils and perhaps will be of similar use.

BIOSTRATIGRAPHY

A fossil has value when it is correctly identified. Certain species have been demonstrated to have lived for only a short interval of time (a few million years or slightly less) and such fossils may be "index fossils" to the age of the rock in which they occur. This was one of the first ways in which fossils were used, and it was with the recognition that each system of rocks had a unique set of fossils, that an orderly sequence of rocks was determined. The development of stratigraphy and the recognition of the sequence of geologic time was possible on the basis of fossils (Fig. 2).

More than 100 years ago, men began to recognize the value and importance of identification and classification of the rocks of the earth. Each rock layer, like the pages of a history book, contained part of the record of the history of the earth. No single place on earth contained all of the "pages" in their correct chronological sequence, but like pages of some giant loose-leaf notebook whose pages had been placed out of sequence, mountain building and erosion had jumbled the rock layers of the earth. Before the history could be chronologically interpreted, these layers had to be identified in their correct sequence.

At first, the work of "reassembling" was not particularly orderly and thus the Cambrian rocks were designated as those rocks which had the same kinds of fossils as a series of rocks in the Cambria Province of Wales while Permian rocks could be identified as those whose fossils were similar to the fossils found in rocks around Perm on the west flank of the Ural Mountains in Russia. The names of the systems of rocks were usually taken from some geographic point where that particular kind of rock was first studied. The recognition and correlation of sections of rocks of the same age but separated geographically from the "type area" were on the basis of the unique fossils of the type area. In this way, the geologic time scale was developed. At first, estimates as to duration of geologic time periods, the time during which a system of rocks was formed, were made on the basis of thickness of rock and the amount of evolution of the contained fossils. Recent advances in geochemistry and radioisotope age determinations have revised the original estimates and we now have a better absolute determination for each Period of geologic time. Radioactive isotopes which can be used for age determination are not as widespread as fossils and time correlations are still established principally on the basis of fossils, at least in the sedimentary rocks of the earth (Fig. 2).

PALEOGEOGRAPHY AND PALEOBIOGEOGRAPHY

A geographic map is a visual representation of land and water and other geographic features of some sector of the earth at the present time. A paleogeographic map is a map which portrays the ancient or paleogeography at a particular time in the geologic past. Such maps may be based largely on fossil determinations of age. Maps thus prepared, showing geographic conditions as they existed during some interval of the past, in one sense, represent the ultimate aim of geologic investigation; that is, the determination of the history of the earth for each shortest possible interval of geologic time.

Related to such determinations are paleobiogeographic studies which are concerned with the geographic distribution of organisms during the geologic past. Such investigations, never complete unless a good representation of every animal which lived is found and described, give good ideas of organic relationships of the past, migration belts and even climatic associations. If studies are performed with fossil organisms whose environmental requirements are known, some idea of paleoclimates can result. Of particular significance for work of this kind has been the discovery that certain plants which today are restricted to rather narrow temperate belts, had a different distribution during the geologic past. For example, floras from Carboniferous and Jurassic rocks of Spitsbergen (80°N latitude) show temperate, almost tropic characteristics, completely unlike arctic vegetation today. Similar observations have aided in the understanding of glacial climates, their extent and the warmer conditions which existed between periods of glaciation.

PALEOECOLOGY

Many of the studies discussed previously can be considered as representing some type of paleoecologic investigation. Paleoecology, in its broadest sense, is the study of the relationships and interrelationships of a fossil organism to all of the factors in its environment — physical, chemical, and organic. Broad paleobiogeographic studies have been accomplished for years and today geologists and paleontologists are making increased use of chemical techniques in order to obtain even better interpretations. The detail thus provided is more specific and of unusually greater value. Of particular importance in such investigations has been the use of oxygen and carbon isotopes. These investigations are based on the chemical principle that aquatic organisms which secrete a calcareous shell, utilize the calcium, oxygen, carbon, etc., of the water in which they live for production of their shell. Among other things, the ratio of "regular" oxygen (O^{16}) and its isotope (O^{18}), taken into the shell is related to the temperature of the water. Therefore, determination of the amount of O^{16} and O^{18} in a shell may give a reliable figure for the actual temperature of the water at the time that part of the shell was secreted. All shells are not preserved well enough to allow such chemical determinations to be made.

A good example of this technique and its value has been provided by study of an extinct squid-like animal which lived during the geologic past. Using the shells of these fossils, as well as those of certain types of clams and oysters, $O^{16} - O^{18}$ determinations were made. Results indicate that the temperature of the water in which these organisms lived had increased gradually through late Mesozoic time and then there was a temperature decrease. Other investigations have shown interesting things concerning individual specimens, e.g. one Jurassic belemnite lived for three summers and four winters (after its youth) and died in the spring of its fourth year. The seasonal spread in temperature during these four years was approximately six degrees centigrade, and the mean temperature of the sea was 17.6°C. All of this information came from a fossil shell more than 60 million years old.

Other significant O^{18} determinations have been made relative to the apparent change in the temperature of the environment of an organism during its growth. Small shelled Foraminifera, a type of Protozoan or one-celled animal, which are abundant in the oceans today, can be studied for isotope chemistry. It has been observed that certain layers of the shell are added at different seasons and depths of water and that observed seasonal differences of living types are related to the temperature and depth factors.

The modern cephalopod, *Nautilus,* is a very difficult animal to study and little was known concerning its early life but $O^{16} - O^{18}$ studies show that the youngest individuals grow in warm water (23° to 28°C) until a certain age at which time the animal migrates rather suddenly to water of approximately 17°C. Thus, data not obtainable from direct observation can be had from shells which are preserved and more accessible after the death of the animal.

Geographic distribution, community association, water temperature and depth are not the only things of interest in the study of paleoecology. Paleosalinities may be determinable from chemical studies, amount of free oxygen in water as it was related to surface turbulence, food dependency of organism, growth patterns, eating habits, and even physiological responses to an environment, are part of the information which may be gleaned in the study of paleoecology, an important area of paleontological research.

By way of summary, it should be emphasized that fossils must be collected, studied and described. This is still the principal contribution of paleontology. The knowledge of patterns of growth and development within populations and between communities can be determined from good descriptions. Evolutionary deveolpment is then often easily discernible. The second step is age determination for biostratigraphic and biogeographic studies, and then ecologic study for paleoclimatologic and paleoecologic information. The amount of data which is obtainable from most good faunas is greater now than ever before because of increased use of the tools of chemistry (organic constituents and isotopes) and physics (paleomagnetism and climatology). Ecologic and biologic data from faunal associations and determinations of the physical environment add more data. With so much data available, the use of modern computers for analysis and correlation has found wide use among paleontologists. Thousands of factors − biologic, ecologic and geologic − can be analyzed in a very few minutes by use of large computers and with the many statistical programs now available. While most of this latter work deals with specific and detailed problems, the answers obtained will undoubtedly have wide interest.

5

Classification and Nomenclature in Paleontology

Animals and plants are classified according to kinship which is often determinable from morphologic characteristics. A system of nomenclature is in use which insures uniformity even in the different languages.

NEED FOR CLASSIFICATION

A system of terminology and a workable classification scheme is important to all students of science. The system of classification and nomenclature of the paleontologist is essentially the same as that of the biologist and serious attempts are made to insure that the usage of nomenclature — biologic and paleobiologic — is uniform.

Classification is essential in all areas of life in order that man can deal with large numbers of items in the most responsible manner. The best classification is one which shows some kind of fundamental relationship between things of a kind (comic strips on one page and sports on another). The classification of organisms is based upon the fundamental premise of biologic kinship or similarity of structure. Hence, all kinds of birds constitute one large but rather closely related group and all kinds of insects another group. The problems of the kinship among fossil groups are not always easy to solve but classification based on morphologic similarity, while far from perfect, is still the basis of most systems.

SYSTEM OF CLASSIFICATION

The fundamental unit of classification in our paleontologic-biologic system is the *species*. Oddly enough, this unit is one of the most difficult to define, at least to the satisfaction of all scientists. A working definition has been that a species consists of a morphologically similar and interbreeding group of organisms (a population) which has fertile offspring. This definition is far from perfect, however, because when the concepts of time and evolution are superimposed, we discover that in those instances where complete lineages are known (ancestors and descendants through millions of years and through many "species") there are many populations which overlap morphologically and reproductively. Hence, species M, at one stage, must have overlapped species L, its ancestor, and because it (species M) gave rise to species N, the descendant, all are linked morphologically and reproductively through time. Where are the population or species boundaries in this example?

As long as relatively few species were known, this was not a problem, but with the resources now available for research, large faunas from many rock sequences in many parts of the world have been discovered and the problem of what constitutes a species is serious.

It is important to visualize, however, that with all of the problems of definition, a species consists of a population of morphologically similar organisms whose ecologic demands and physiologic functions are the same and whose offspring are similar and capable of propagating this same line.

If the definition of a species is difficult, the definition of higher taxa is impossible, for their existence is mostly on paper or in the minds of the taxonomist. Groups of species with an indefinite number of similar characteristics are grouped into a single *genus* (plural, *genera*). The two names, genus first and species second, form the scientific binomial name and every plant and animal, living and fossil, has such a two-name assignment. The idea to give every plant and animal a minimum of two names was adopted after the proposals of the Swedish naturalist Linnaeus, who in 1758 published a catalogue of every known organism using the two-name or *binomial* system.

There is a large system of classification above the generic level, but it is not part of the binomial system and is rarely used by the non-specialist. For instance, similar genera are put together in a single family; families are grouped into orders; orders into classes; and similar classes may comprise a phylum (plural, phyla). The various phyla are classified as either animal or plant, and these designations are called kingdoms, the highest unit of classification. In this scheme of classification, the house cat would be listed as follows:

Kingdom — Animal
Phylum — Vertebrata
Class — Mammalia
Order — Carnivora
Family — Felidae
Genus — Felis
Species — domesticus

Thus the binomial name of the species is *Felis domesticus.*

NOMENCLATURE

A name for an organism, in order to have validity, must conform to the binomial system of nomenclature. The genus and species name must be latinized and proposed by a specialist in certain ways. There is an international commission which is recognized as the ultimate authority and this body issues rules, judgments, etc., concerning problems of classification and nomenclature. This helps to insure a standardization, and Algerians, Russians and South Africans despite differences in language can recognize the scientific names used by others.

A common fossil is the cephalopod *Plesioturrilites brazoensis* (Roemer). The first name is the genus name, the second the species and the third is the name of the author who first described the species. The parenthesis is only put around the authors name if the genus name has been changed since it was first described.

The non-specialist may ask, why the complex name? Why not use the common name for animals and plants and say "horse" instead of *Equus caballus?* The answer is simple. Even in the largest dictionaries there are approximately 500,000 words. Yet more than a million different plants and animals are living today and estimates for the number of species in the past put the figure at more than 500 million. There are not enough common names to go around and they would differ in different languages. Also, some of our common names are less difficult (cow, robin, oyster) but consider boa constrictor or hippopotamus. The point to remember is that names are common if they are familiar, whether or not they are complex.

Some specialists have suggested that even the binomial system is not inclusive enough to handle everything which is known today and complex systems of numbers or letters have been suggested as alternatives to the binomial system.

There are many points of nomenclature with which specialists must be familiar and which even the non-specialist may encounter occasionally. The binomial (genus and species) name is always written in italics, e.g. *Venus mercenaria,* so that it will be easily spotted on a printed page, for example.

CHAPTER

6

Fossils and the Evolution of Plants

The earliest definite life known consists of microscopic aquatic organisms which thrived on earth 2 to 3 billion years ago. These plant-like structures are the oldest known fossils. Some form of aquatic plant life was present during every period of geologic time, but definite land plants did not appear until the early Paleozoic. Most modern floras had a late Mesozoic-Cenozoic origin.

Sedimentary rocks of the earth are literally filled with fossil representatives of all of the major and most of the minor groups of animals and plants living today. In addition, some groups of fossils have no living representatives. Extinction and change have been the story of life since its first days on earth and there are few things living today which are similar to life 600 million years ago when life first became abundant.

Fossil groups are studied according to their kind and size. Invertebrate animals are studied together; vertebrates are studied separately. Plants, as well as spores and pollen, constitute another area of study. It has been estimated that more than 1,130,000 species have been described but that there may have been 500 million species which have lived on the earth.

Although the record of fossil plants does not appear to be as extensive as that of animals, a considerable body of knowledge has accumulated concerning origin of plants and their geologic history. This study, paleobotany, is one of the most rapidly developing "paleo" disciplines, especially because of the increased use of fossil spores and pollen in solving geologic problems. A great diversity of types has already been discovered in Paleozoic rocks and paleobotanists have turned their attention to Precambrian rocks for some indication of

ultimate origins. Such investigations have been successful and just a
few years ago, the late Professor S. Tyler of the University of Wisconsin
discovered abundant primitive plant types of the fungi-algae group in
Precambrian rocks of southern Canada which are associated with material which has been radioactively dated as two billion years old. Not
only were Precambrian plants confirmed by this discovery but of equal
significance is the fact that this was the oldest known structurally

CHART 1. Development of the principal plant groups and their distribution
through time.

preserved life, animal or plant (Fig. 4). Some paleontologists have
ranked this discovery as one of the great discoveries of this century.
More recently, Professor Barghoorn of Harvard University, who continued the work initiated by Dr. Tyler, has found similar primitive
fungi-algae types — all microscopic — in South African rocks thought

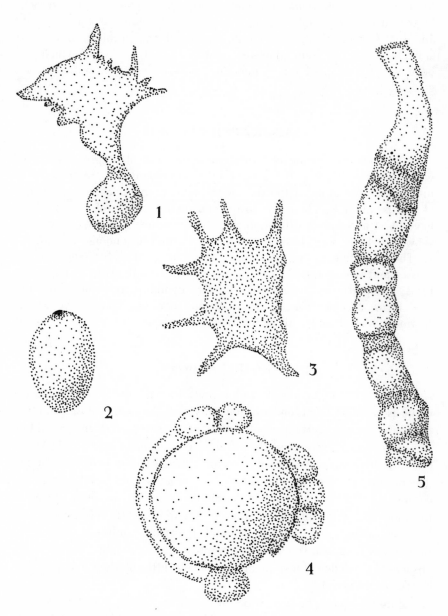

Figure 4. Oldest known plants. Unusual rod and globular bodies from Precambrian of Canada here magnified approximately 1500 X (adapted from Barghoorn and Tyler.)

to be three billion years old. These discoveries lend strong argument
to the idea that primitive plant types were the earliest forms of life
and that higher plants as well as certain of the primitive one-celled
animals originated from plant-like material. This is a view which has
been widely accepted but which only now is being substantiated by
geologic discoveries.

CLASSIFICATION OF PLANTS

The general scheme of evolution within the plant group is fairly
well understood although the rigorous requirements for preservation of
fossils have not allowed the record of plants to be as complete as that
of marine animals. There are 15 or more major groups of plants which
have lived and the classification is rather complex. A simplified outline
shows at least four basic groups, not formal taxonomic categories:
1. The primitive types, including algae, fungi, and for convenience,
mosses and liverworts, 2. the Pteridophytes, including the psilophytes,
ferns, lycopods, and horsetails, 3. the gymnosperms, including the
seed ferns, cycads, ginkgos, cordaites and conifers, and 4. the angiosperms, which includes all of the flowering plants.

PRIMITIVE PLANTS

The algae, fungi, mosses and a few other groups in which woody
tissue is reduced or absent are generally considered the most primitive
types. No one is certain what relationship exists between the oldest
life forms which were recently recognized in Canada and South Africa
and primitive algal-like fossil structures which have been known for
generations. It is of importance to note that so little is known concerning the biology of the algal-like material that it is becoming popular
to study this material in terms of its environment rather than of its
botanical affinities. The environmental approach, while not completely
satisfactory from a taxonomic viewpoint, is perhaps realistic in terms of
absolute knowledge. Most fossil algae have little of their recognizable
structure preserved.

Primitive types of pod, tube, and sphere-shaped forms are known
but the record of well preserved early plants is still scant. There is
little evidence of relationships to other groups.

An interesting member of the moss group is illustrated in Fig. 5.
Bryophyta such as this are not well known.

PTERIDOPHYTES—FIRST VASCULAR PLANTS

Next highest on the evolutionary ladder of plants are the first vascular types — plants which had some form of woody tissue. The oldest definite vascular types are those described from Silurian rocks. Recently, unusual Cambrian plants have been discovered in India, Kashmir and Russia, which may be closely related to the Silurian types and, if not vascular, perhaps ancestral. There appears to be no general agreement on the significance of these discoveries yet.

Primitive vascular types consist of wood, a central pith, and, in addition, usually two thin layers of different cells which are external to the wood. Early types include forms called psilophytes and are illustrated by *Rhynia,* a dichotomously branching form which stood from a few inches high to a foot or more with no true root system and branches without true leaves (Fig. 5). These early types reproduced by means of spores — microscopic bodies which were produced in great numbers by sporangia at the top of the branches. Such types were abundant in the Late Silurian and Devonian Periods and it was during the Devonian that the first development of land plants occurred.

Evolution was rapid and by the Middle Devonian, the first forests with large trees developed. These forests consisted of, in addition to *Rhynia* types, ferns, horsetails and lycopods or club mosses.

Fern-like plants which appeared in the Devonian were probably ancestral to true ferns today. Carboniferous ferns were so abundant that the Carboniferous has been called the "Age of Ferns" just as the Devonian has been called the "Age of Forests." In both instances, those who dubbed these periods of times with such titles were a bit too enthusiastic. Many of the Carboniferous ferns have proved to be simply "fern-like" structures called "preferns" by some writers and most are from a relatively restricted part of the Carboniferous system.

Some of the Carboniferous ferns left magnificent fossils. Impressions and compressions of stems, leaves, roots and complete plants, 25-50 feet or more in height, have been found (Fig. 6). Fossil fern leaf types are diverse but similarities with modern types can be seen (Fig. 7). Fern leaves either of this type or of the more advanced seed ferns are among the most common plant fossils found.

The lycopods or club mosses are a third group of Paleozoic plants. *Lepidodendron,* the so-called scale tree, is one of the most common types (Fig. 8). These trees stood 100 feet or more, had thick trunks and are distinguished by an extensive underground root system (Figs. 8 & 9) and especially by a curious pattern of leaf scars on the trunk. The leaves were attached along the length of their base and when

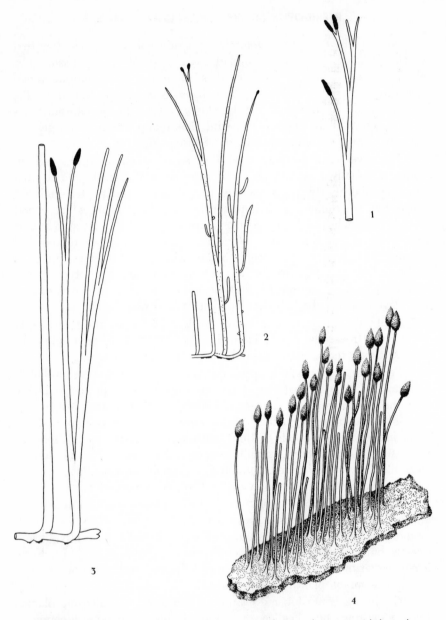

Figure 5. Primitive plants. 1-3. **Rhynia,** a simple vascular type with branching stalks which bear single reproductive bodies. Approximately one foot high (after Darrah); 4. Restoration of a primitive moss, **Sporogonites exuberans,** approximately six inches long, from the Devonian of Belgium. This primitive form shows unbranched stalks and had no vascular tissue (after Andrews).

Figure 6. Reconstruction of a Pennsylvanian fern tree. Below the fronds can be seen leaf scars on this 25 foot tree. Most of the trunk encased in adventitious roots which thicken toward the base (after Andrews).

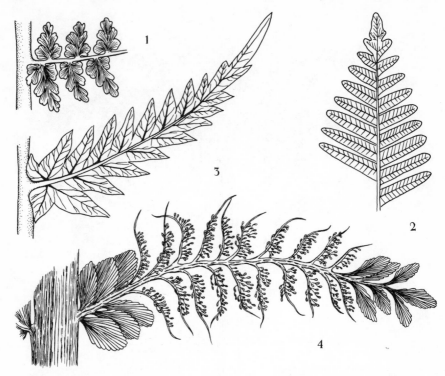

Figure 7. Paleozoic ferns. 1. **Sphenopteris;** 2. **Mariopteris;** 3. **Pecopteris,**
all Pennsylvanian ferns approximately natural size (after Darrah); 4. **Archaeopteris hibernica,** an Upper Devonian primitive fern with fertile pinnules in
middle part (after Andrews).

they were shed, left a prominent type scar (Fig. 10). The spiral arrangement of these scars gave a peculiar pattern to the trunks.

The last major group of pteridophytes is the horsetail or arthro-
phyte group including the *Calamites-Annularia* types (Fig. 10). These
were tree sized plants, some 30 to 50 feet high, whose trunks were
characteristically composed of a series of segments, superficially like
modern cane. Limbs diverged upward at each segment of the stem and
leaves branched off from these (Fig. 11). Some of the trunks attained
diameters of several feet.

GYMNOSPERMS

A varied group of non-flowering plants still abundant today are
the gymnosperms. This group includes several types which may not

Figure 8. Restorations of **Lepidodendron,** the scale tree, a Pennsylvanian lycopod; young tree before branching and older one approximately 100 feet high (after Andrews).

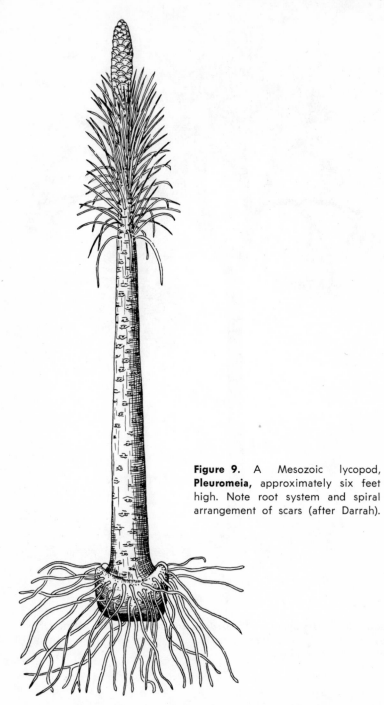

Figure 9. A Mesozoic lycopod, **Pleuromeia,** approximately six feet high. Note root system and spiral arrangement of scars (after Darrah).

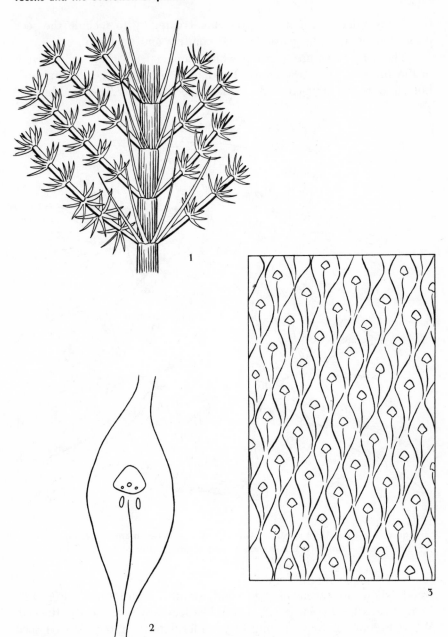

Figure 10. **Annularia,** a common Pennsylvanian calamitid type, approximately one-half natural size (after Darrah); 2., 3. **Lepidodendron** branch exterior approximately to scale. Notice spiral pattern and details in side diagram which shows scar enlarged (adapted from Andrews).

be closely related, but it is a convenient category to include the seed ferns, cycads, ginkgos, cordaites and conifers and gnetophytes.

The seed ferns are a group which ranged from the Carboniferous to the Jurassic. This group was abundant during these geologic periods but all were extinct before the end of the Mesozoic. The seed-bearing

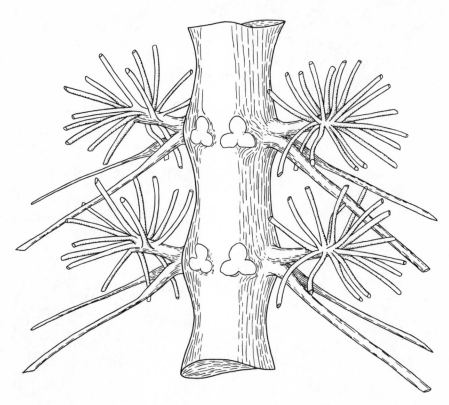

Figure 11. An Upper Pennsylvanian horsetail, **Bowmanites fertilis,** from Illinois, approximately 2 1/2 inches long (after Andrews).

fronds show advancement over more primitive fern types (Fig. 12). Many fossils have been found of fern-like leaves with no seeds attached. Whether some of these belong to the pteridophyte group or true seed ferns has been a question. Some of these common types are shown in Figure 12.

Cycads, cordaites and conifers, and gnetophytes are important kinds which have left a good geologic record (Fig. 13). The conifers in-

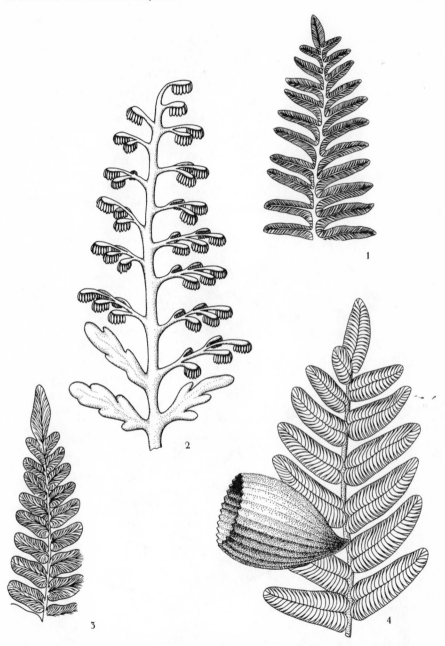

Figure 12. Seed ferns of the Pennsylvanian. 1. **Alethopteris;** 3. **Neuropteris,** approximately to scale (from Darrah); 2. **Crossotheca** sp., restoration of Illinois specimen (X2) (after Andrews); 4. Neuropterid type with reproductive body. Specimen from Holland (X2) (after Andrews).

Figure 13.   A Pennsylvanian cordaitean branch with reproductive bodies in leaf axials. Some cordaites were more than 100 feet high (after Andrews).

cluding pines, firs, spruce, redwoods and others, include more than 500 species, approximately 80 percent of all living gymnosperms. Several families were abundant from the Pennsylvanian to the Recent. The Arizona Petrified Forest of the Triassic age is primarily a conifer forest and 42 species of conifers and other types have been identified there. The conifers are one of the most successful groups of plants.

The ginkgo has often been described as a "living fossil." This unusual plant (Fig. 14) was abundant in many parts of the world during the late Paleozóic, Mesozoic and early Cenozoic. It became extinct in North America during the Miocene and during the Pliocene in Europe. Some 19 genera were known before this extinction. In the early 1700's, ginkgos were discovered growing in eastern China where they had

Figure 14. The living ginkgo, **Ginkgo biloba.** Leaves and seeds are similar to fossil types which became extinct in North America and Europe during the Middle and Late Cenozoic. The ginkgo has been reintroduced by man in these areas, one-half natural size (after Andrews).

been cultivated for centuries in Chinese gardens. The plant was transplanted to Europe and then back to North America and now is becoming a popular shade tree.

Gymnosperms appeared in the late Paleozoic and spread rapidly until the middle Cenozoic. Since then, restriction and extinction have been common patterns.

ANGIOSPERMS

The flowering plants or angiosperms appeared during the Mesozoic and are a dominant part of late Mesozoic and Cenozoic floras. This group contains common dicotyledon characteristics and most of the plants are familiar to everyone — the oaks, maples, walnuts, poplars, birch, hickory, sycamores, magnolias, ivy, etc.; in addition to the dicotyledon types, there are the monocotyledons, such as grasses, cereals, etc.

Cretaceous leaves, representatives of extinct but familiar plants, are shown in Figure 15. Reports of angiosperms in Triassic and Jurassic rocks are still being studied but definite Cretaceous forms are widespread. An upper Cretaceous flora from Alaska of more than 200 species included 15 genera of gymnosperms but 73 genera of angiosperms. The evolution of the group shows enormous diversification and radiation of species. Angiosperms have been the dominant part of most floras since their appearance.

Flowering types reproduce by means of pollen, tiny germinating microcells. These remarkable reproductive parts are readily preserved in non-oxidizing environments and fossil pollen as well as spores from more primitive types are exceedingly abundant in rocks of Paleozoic to Recent age. Their study is so specialized that a specific area of study called palynology has developed. Certain types are apparently useful in biostratigraphic work and their study for paleoclimatological determinations is especially important (Fig. 16).

PLANTS AND CLIMATES OF THE PAST

Plant environment has special importance for interpretation of earth history. Most higher plants are rather sensitive indicators of their environments. Characteristic floras are found only in certain ecologic systems. Today's floras can be interpreted in terms of their present ecologic requirements and these same conditions can be assumed for like floras of previous time intervals. Thus, the breadfruit, *Artocarpus*, today lives within 20 degrees of latitude from the Equator. This same plant is found fossilized in the Upper Cretaceous of Greenland which

Figure 15. A Cretaceous angiosperm leaf, **Aspidophyllum,** approximately natural size (after Darrah).

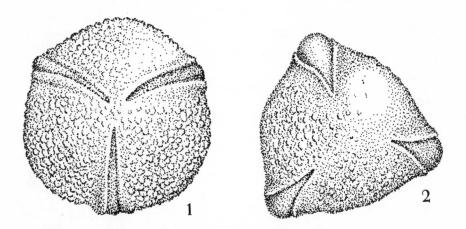

Figure 16. Pollen grains form angiosperms. 1. beech; and 2. oak; approximately .03mm. in diameter (after Wodehouse).

is above 60 degrees north latitude. Eocene floras of California and Oregon are most similar to those found today in Central America where 80 inches of rainfall a year and no freezing temperatures are common. Thus, floras may be utilized for determinations of climates of the past.

CHAPTER

7

Invertebrates

The animals without backbones (invertebrates) evolved during the late Precambrian but were not abundant until approximately 600 million years ago. From that time until now, millions of species have lived and died, leaving a fantastic record of evolution. Most of the general patterns of evolution of the invertebrates have been determined. The contribution of invertebrates to the study of ancient environments is remarkable.

There are approximately a dozen phyla of geologically important invertebrates. Approximately 80 percent of the 130,000 or so known fossil animals are invertebrates. More students study invertebrates and more is known about this category than is known about any other fossil group. They are probably the most useful group in the interpretation of earth history.

PHYLUM PROTOZOA

The one-celled animal group includes structurally simple animals but certain members of the group are neither so simple nor primitive. Although the known number of species, living and fossil, is approximately 36,000 or three percent of all known animal species, in terms of volume, this phylum would outbulk all of the other invertebrates. Apparently, no animals have a longer geologic history and their Precambrian to Recent range makes them one of the most important fossil groups.

Most protozoans have no hard parts and one would not anticipate finding a fossil *Amoeba* or *Euglena*. There are several groups which possess a shell structure and one of these, the Foraminifera, is geologically important.

The body of protozoans consists of a bit of protoplasm which contains one or more nuclei and various other structures. Locomotion is accomplished in a variety of ways and the classification of the phylum is based on locomotor structures. Protozoans are found in all environments but most are aquatic.

Protozoans are usually classified into four large groups: Sporozoans, flagellates, ciliates and sarcodinids. No fossil sporozoans (parasitic types) are known but the shelled flagellates including coccoliths, dinoflagellates, discoasters (see frontispiece) and silicoflagellates, are abundant. Fossil ciliates include the tintinnids with a trumpet-shaped but microscopic shell (Fig. 17). The sarcodinids, including two large groups, the Foraminifera and the Radiolaria, are especially important.

Foraminifera

Most Foraminifera have a shell less than a millimeter in size which is an original secretion of calcium carbonate ($CaCO_3$) or may consist of organic material or may be formed by the agglutinization of debris and held together by one of several cementing agents. The calcareous shelled types are the most abundant today and have been since the Mississippian. The shell may consist of a single chamber or, more commonly, a series of chambers which indicate progressive size increase (Fig. 17). Foraminifera have always been marine animals and have been extremely abundant in the past as well as at present. Studies concerning living types show that some species reproduce 20-30 offspring at monthly intervals, of which each individual is capable of doing the same thing within a month of its birth. Free floating and swimming, as well as bottom dwelling types of Foraminifera are known.

The earliest Foraminifera were simple types and the group was not particularly abundant until the late Paleozoic when calcareous wheat grain-shaped forms evolved. Other more modern types of Foraminifera became abundant shortly after. Ancestors of the abundant types which can be found in today's oceans are known in Mesozoic and Cenozoic rock (Fig. 17). They are so abundant and were so rapidly evolving that they have found widespread use in petroleum exploration as index fossils.

Study of the shells of Recent and Pleistocene Foraminifera has given us considerable information concerning the Recent Ice Ages. Cores taken from various sites in the Atlantic contain a rather complete record of Foraminifera. One species of *Globigerina, G. truncatulinoides,* has a shell which coils in one direction if the animal lives in cold water and coils in the opposite direction if the water temperature is warm. The alternating sequences of left and right coiled shells which have been

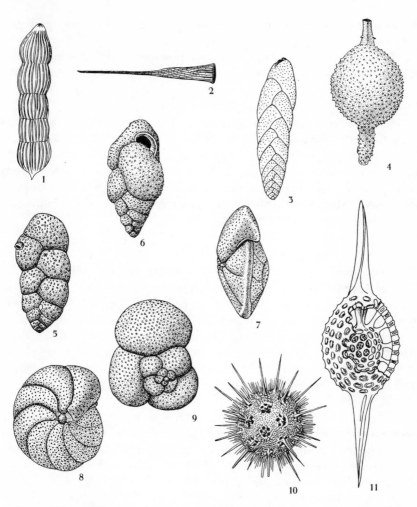

Figure 17. Fossil protozoans; Foraminifera, radiolarians, and tintinnids. 1, 3-9 are Foraminifera; 1. **Dentalina crosswickensis,** a straight five chambered form (X46), Early Cenozoic; 3. **Loxostoma plaitum,** chambers arranged side by side as well as vertically (X61), Cretaceous; 4. **Dentalina pseudoaculeata,** straight bulbous type (X98), Early Cenozoic; 5. **Gaudryina monmouthensis,** notice location of aperture below shell apex (X53), Cretaceous; 6. **Chiloguembelina crinita,** notice large aperture laterally situated (X141), Early Cenozoic; 7, 8. side and front views of **Cibicides harperi,** planispirally coiled form (X80), Cretaceous; 9. **Globigerina inaequispira,** spiral arrangement of chambers (X98), Early Cenozoic (adapted from Olsson); 2. a Recent tintinnid, **Rhabdonella conica** (X100); 10, 11. radiolarians. 10. globular type with spines, **Haeckeliana darwiniana,** Recent (X50); 11. elongate type with outer shell broken to expose inner capsule, **Stylatractus giganteus,** Recent (X100), (after Campbell and Moore).

found in sediment cores provide interesting clues to duration and geographic extent of glacial climatic fluctuations.

Other species of Foraminifera have provided a rather complete and
reliable series of zones for use in world wide correlation of rock strata.

Radiolaria

The Radiolarians are protozoans with a silica (SiO_2) test of less
geologic significance. Their geologic range is Precambrian to Recent.
They are small (less than one millimeter) but several thousand species
have been described. The shell structure is a hollow siliceous body
with perforations (Fig. 17). The living animal occupies both sides of
the sphere. Most radiolarians were apparently free-floating organisms.

PHYLUM PORIFERA

The sponges and sponge-like organisms are the simplest multi-
cellular animals. The sponges are sessile, aquatic, variable in shape and
are commonly colonial. Most living and fossil sponges were small
(only a few inches in diameter) but forms with a body diameter of
more than three feet are known. There are probably 2,000 living species.
Approximately 2,000 fossil species are known. Because of their porous
body, sponges were not preserved as readily as other invertebrate groups
and except in locally abundant areas, they are considered to be rare
fossils.

The earliest record of sponges is based on parts of the internal
skeleton which have been found in Late Precambrian rocks. Most people
are aware of sponges because of the general commercial use of their
soft parts as household cleaning aids, but disease and unchecked commercial exploitation have threatened the existence of many large sponge
communities in modern seas.

Sponges do not have a rigid external skeleton but a rather soft
three layered body, the inner layer of which may contain a skeleton
composed of siliceous, calcareous, or organic spicules. The body is generally rounded and porous and water enters the hollow center through
the pores and exits through a central opening often called the "mouth."
In the process food is picked up by cells of the inner wall. The skeleton,
when present, may be firmly formed of interlocking spicules (Fig. 18)
or the spicules may be loose in the flesh and serve as supports. Scattered spicules are more common fossils than a whole skeleton (Fig. 18).

A few spicules have been obtained from Precambrian rocks. Lower
Paleozoic forms are generally rare but are commonly bowl, pillar and
vase shaped structures (Fig. 18). One sponge-like group occurs in

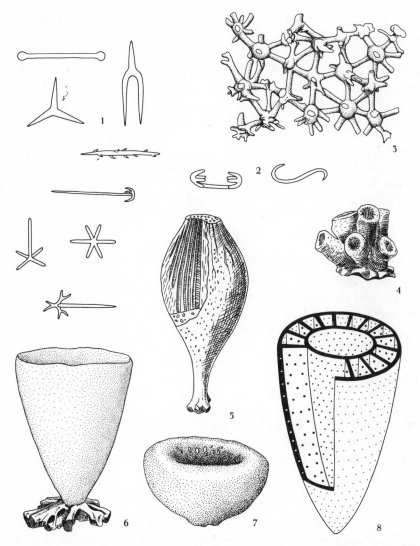

Figure 18. Sponges, sponge spicules, and sponge-like animals. 1. eight kinds of spicules of siliceous sponges, the large variety (X100); 2. Two kinds of small siliceous sponge spicules (X1,000); 3. United spicule group of the sponge **Astylospongia praemorsa** from the Silurian of Germany magnified 100 times; 4. A calcareous sponge, **Eusiphonella bronni** from the Jurassic of Europe (X1); 5. wall structure in **Acrochordonia ramosa** from the Cretaceous of Germany (X30); 6. vase-shaped siliceous sponge from the Cretaceous of Europe (X1/2); 7. bowl-type sponge from the Silurian of Germany (X3/4); 8. diagrammatic view of an archaeocyathid sponge-like animal with inner and outer walls and vertical partitions. Note inner cavity and numerous pores, sketch greatly enlarged (from Okulitch and de Laubenfels).

Cambrian rocks in many parts of the world and is called Archaeo-cyathids. They are one to four inch structures which once lived in reef-like conditions parallel to the coastlines of ancient seas. Typical forms are vase shaped (Fig. 18) consisting of two walls between which were vertical partitions. Walls and partitions were porous and there was a central cavity.

Modern sponges are found in warm equatorial waters and they range to the polar regions. All are aquatic and most are marine. Spicular skeletons make them an unpopular part of most diets but they are known to be eaten by a few kinds of snails and fishes. Their hollow center forms a protected cavity for certain crustaceans, parasites and other animals. Starfish have been found preserved in the cavity of fossil sponges and this type of association is known today.

PHYLUM COELENTERATA

This large and diverse group includes the corals, the jellyfishes, the hydras and their kin. Some are microscopic and others range to six feet in length and may have tentacles 130 feet long. Even with this diversity it is curious to note that most coelenterates are constructed on a uni-form pattern. This pattern is a simple sack-shaped body with a three layered wall surrounding a large gastrovascular cavity (stomach-like structure) which contains no internal viscera. The mouth is located at one end and is surrounded by a group of tentacles, usually in cycles of 2, 4, 6 or 8. Several important coelenterate types have skeletons (Fig. 19) while others have no hard parts.

There are three major groups or classes of Coelenterata: Class Hydrozoa (simple types), Class Anthozoa (Corals and sea anemones), and Class Scyphozoa (true jellyfish).

Class Hydrozoa

The simplest and presumably most primitive Coelenterate group includes small fresh water and marine soft-bodied forms. Small solitary types such as *Hydra* as well as large colonial forms such as the Portu-guese Man-of-War bear stinging capsules which are used for protection and for aid in capturing prey. Most hydrozoans have no skeleton and have not been preserved as fossils. A few groups secreted a calcareous skeleton such as certain reef builders during the Silurian and Devonian. Their skeleton had the form of irregular, rounded masses with relatively thin sheet-like expansions penetrated by the tubular remains of the animal. Cambrian to Recent types are known and similar calcareous types are common on coral reefs today.

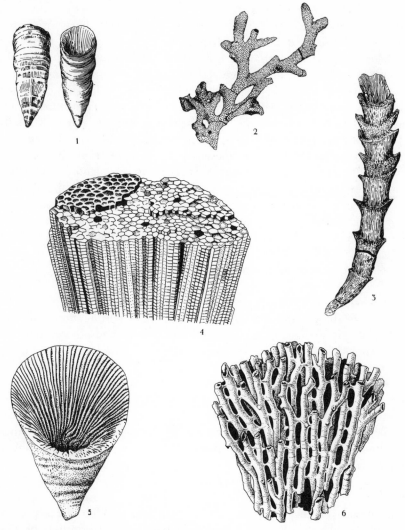

Figure 19. Corals of the Paleozoic. 1. A rugose coral, **Holophragma calceoloides** from the Silurian of Gotland (X2), showing wrinkled or rugose nature and deep cup; 2. **Alveolites winchellana,** surface view of a tabulate coral from the Devonian of Kentucky (X1/2); 3. **Blothrophyllum greeni,** a rugose form showing evidence of pauses in growth from the Devonian of Kentucky (X1/2); 4. a large tabulate colony showing cross section of individuals and transverse tabula; **Favosites gothlandicus,** Silurian (X1); 5. **Kionelasma conspicuum.** A rugose coral showing vertical septa in cup, Devonian of Kentucky (X1); 6. A tabulate colony showing discrete yet connected individuals, **Syringopora ramulosa,** Lower Carboniferous of Belgium (X1) (1, 4, 6, after Bayer et al., 2, 3, 5, after Stumm).

Class Scyphozoa and Conulariids

The true jellyfish is of minor geologic importance. These organisms have an umbrella or saucer shaped body from which hang the tentacles and mouth parts. All are marine and swim freely near the ocean surface in their adult stage. Their geologic record is poor because most individuals contain less than one percent solid matter. Questionable impressions have been reported from the Precambrian and younger rocks but definite fossil jellyfish are among the rarest of fossils.

One extinct group of fossils which may be similar to scyphozoans but which possesses shells is known to have lived from Cambrian to Triassic. Typically, these conulariids consists of slender pyramidal shaped structures, quadrate in cross-section and bearing prominent transverse markings on the outer surface (Fig. 20). Some specimens have been found with what appear to be impressions of tentacles extending from the larger end. This has suggested that the conulariids represent the shell of a jellyfish-like floating or swimming animal. The question of their exact relationship remains unanswered.

Class Anthozoa

This is the largest and geologically most important group of coelenterates. More than 6,000 living species are known, all marine. This group includes the corals, sea pens, sea anemones, etc. Geologically, the most significant anthozoans are the rugose and tabulate corals of the Paleozoic. Most members of these groups were small but colonial forms several feet in diameter are known. The rugose corals are often called horn corals because of the similarity of their shape to that of a small horn (Fig. 19). Most are small, cone shaped, and the most important skeletal features are the radial plates, called septa, which project from the wall of the "cone" to the center of the specimen (Fig. 19). In many types, additional plates called tabulae grow transversely to the septa (Fig. 19). These tabulae are the important structural feature of the so-called tabulate corals in which the septa are reduced or absent. Because these animals grew by addition of new material on old, all stages of life are preserved in complete specimens and the ontogeny, or early life history of an individual, can be readily understood (Fig. 19). The different patterns of growth shown by the septa have been the basis of their classification and all rugose corals with the same kind of septa are grouped together as one family.

Both rugose and tabulates appeared during the Ordovician and became extinct in the late Permian or earliest Triassic. Warm, more or less normal marine shallow water, similar to that necessary for modern day corals, was probably the environment for the Paleozoic types.

Geologically, they first became widespread in the Silurian, declined until another evolutionary burst in the Devonian and then there was a gradual decline in number until extinction in the late Permian.

After the Paleozoic the Scleractinia, or stony corals became abundant. They first appeared in the Middle Triassic. Whether they evolved from a rugose ancestor or from a separate line of shelless Paleozoic ane-

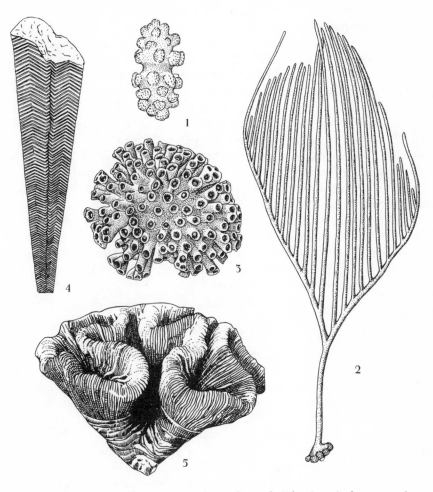

Figure 20. Octocorals, stony corals, and conulariids. 1. spicule, approximately .05 mm., from a modern octocoral; 2. **Ctenocella pectinata** approximately (X1/4), Pacific form; 3. a modern stony coral colony, **Duncanopsammia axifuga,** (X1/4) from Australia; 4. **Paraconularia worthi,** a Permian conularid from India (X1); 5. modern stony coral colony, **Trachyphyllia geoffroyi** (X1/2), Australia (after Bayer et al.).

mones is unknown. All of the modern "true" corals, so common on the flourishing reefs in the temperate marine waters of the world, are of this type. Various modifications in arrangement of septa, development of a colonial habit, etc., can be observed from a study of scleractinids of the Mesozoic and Cenozoic (Fig. 20). Today, this group grows best in water at approximately 25°C. Water is needed which is shallow enough to allow plenty of sunshine to penetrate (less than 600 feet) and in which a moderate amount of water circulation occurs.

Another important modern group is the octocorals, soft bodied types which possess a loose network of $CaCO_3$ sclerites for a skeleton (Fig. 20). Few whole skeletons are found but the amount of sclerite material being deposited today has been estimated at a ton per year in areas where octocorals are abundant.

Corals are among the most common fossils found in Paleozoic rocks almost everywhere in the world but are less widespread in Mesozoic and Cenozoic rocks. Large colonial types with a broad base are commonly found in place and in the Middle Devonian coral beds of the Rhine area in Germany, massive coral heads, more than three feet in diameter are still found in their original position of growth, some 380 million years after their death.

Coral reefs which are mound like structures built by organic activity are an impressive part of the geologic record. During the Silurian, massive as well as smaller reefs grew in the seas which covered much of the area of Iowa, Wisconsin, Illinois and Indiana. Devonian reefs are found in many parts of the world.

PHYLUM BRYOZOA

One of the least conspicuous major groups of invertebrates is the group of sessile (attached) animals known as bryozoans or ectoprocts. These tiny colonial animals are commonly encountered as encrustations on rocks or on other shells and certain types have the appearance of a perforated plate or sieve (Fig. 21). Each tiny opening of the "sieve" housed a single individual whose soft parts are lost after death. The houses are little more than a cave in a calcareous mass but they are all that remains for paleontologic study (Fig. 21).

There are approximately 3,000 living species and these animals were equally abundant during the geologic past. The first bryozoans appeared in the Ordovician and although certain kinds were very abundant during intervals of the past, bryozoans have never been considered as geologically important invertebrates.

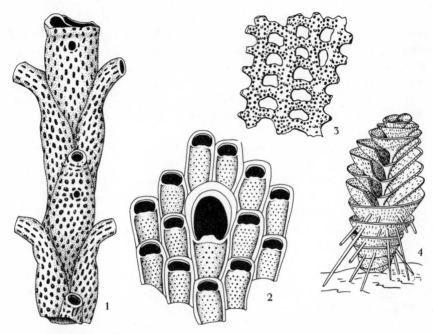

Figure 21. Bryozoans (Ectoprocta). 1. **Tubucellaria vicksburgica,** mode of growth in Eocene colony from Gulf Coast (X25); 2. **Steginoporella jacksonica,** individuals of colony with large apertures, Eocene, Gulf Coast (X25) (after Cheetham); 3. **Septopora subquadrans,** small openings of individuals and larger "windows" through colony (X5), Mississippian, North America; 4. **Archimedes** sp., a diagrammatic illustration of lace-like frond around a stony axis, Mississippian-Pennsylvanian of North America (X1) (after Easton).

Most are marine and all are aquatic. An individual may be less than one millimeter in length but great colonies are known with combined skeletal structure of more than a foot in diameter. The animal had a tiny sack-shaped body with a cluster of tentacles surrounding a mouth. Principal in the body structure is a "U" shaped digestive tube which returns the anus to a position near the mouth on the upper surface of the animal. Sets of muscles allow the body to be pulled into or pushed out of the tubular skeleton. Most are bisexual and produce egg and sperm in different parts of their body. Free swimming larvae may settle and form a new colony. Other types reproduce by budding which increases the size of the colony (Fig. 21). Food consists of microscopic organic material which can be gathered by the mouth tentacles.

The most important groups which lived during the Paleozoic were extinct by the end of the Permian but two other groups which evolved during the Paleozoic plus a group which originated in the Jurassic are living today.

Unusual Paleozoic types include *Archimedes* (Fig. 21) with a large stony axis and a delicate lace-like colonial network swirling around this core as well as a lacey variety (Fig. 21) not associated with a stony axis.

The evolution of a more or less lowly group of animals such as the bryozoans is difficult to evaluate. The sudden appearance of a new species or genus in a vertical rock sequence more often reflects a shift in environmental factors and the organisms which come with such environments than a positive evolutionary lineage. Evolution becomes the product and resultant of many such environmental shifts but fossil bryozoan studies are not advanced enough to clearly define many trends.

Living types are found from pole to pole and down to 18,000 feet or more but the greatest abundance is in shallow seas of tropical or at least temperate zones.

GRAPTOLITES

The degree of understanding that we have for most fossil groups is based largely on our understanding of living representatives of the particular group. This dependency between fossil and living types is well illustrated when we deal with extinct groups. Fossil graptolites are rather common in Ordovician and Silurian and Lower Devonian rocks the world over and have proved to be one of the best index fossils for rocks of this age. The group lived until the lower Carboniferous and then became extinct. No form of life living today has the same structure as the graptolites and although a group of pterobranchs, vertebrate related "chordate-like" animals, are similar, some authorities insist that the similarities are only superficial and that graptolites of the Lower Paleozoic are unique. Although a chordate affinity appears valid, some biologists still think that the graptolites are an extinct kind of bryozoan, or coelenterate, or represent an extinct phylum.

Because none of the "soft parts" or vital organs are known to be preserved, the precise functions of the animal can only be guessed, for all that has been preserved is the empty "house" which the animal occupied (Fig. 22).

We know that graptolites were colonial and marine. We know that they produced an organic (chitinoid) external skeleton which consisted of a series of cups or chambers arranged along a central stalk and that each cup housed an animal. Most fossil specimens are little more than carbon impressions although distinctive shapes are known (Fig. 22). The individual cup is microscopic but the large colonies may be several inches across (Fig. 22). Material illustrating detailed structure of graptolites has been etched from limestone by means of hydrofluoric acid. The initial point of growth is a small cup-like structure from which additional growth by branching takes place. New branches bear individual cup-shaped structures which house individuals (Fig. 22). Each

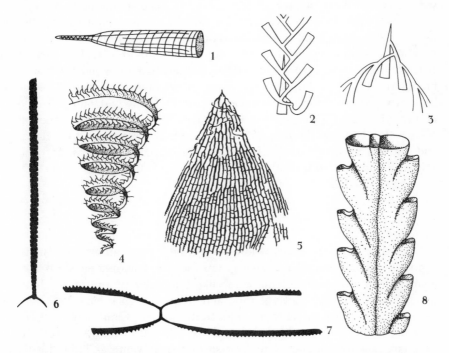

Figure 22. Graptolites. 1. embryonic part of graptolite colony from which budding of individuals occurs, the prosicula (X50); 2 and 3. two growth patterns from prosicula, one showing downward or primitive pattern, the other upward or advanced; diagrammatic; 4. an unusual graptolite colony, **Monograptus turriculatus** from the Lower Silurian of Bohemia (X2); 5. a primitive colony showing numerous branches and downward direction of growth, **Dictyonema flabelliforme** (X1/2); 6. an advanced type, **Climacograptus bicornis** (X1), Middle Ordovician, illustrates most typical preservation pattern; 7. colony with four branches, **Tetragraptus approximatus** (X2), Ordovician of Sweden; 8. enlarged part of **Glyptograptus** colony to illustrate individual cups of animals and growth relationship (X15) (after Bulman).

genus developed a particular growth pattern and this pattern is the basis of classification for most types.

Both sessile and floating types are known but most of the geologically important types were floating colonies. This also seems to explain the widespread abundance of graptolites in black shale, sediment deposited under conditions apparently inhospitable to most forms of life.

Of considerable significance in graptolite studies has been the recognition of several rather well-defined evolutionary trends in the whole group. These group trends can be related to stratigraphic sequences with a considerable degree of success and hence, graptolites are recognized as one of the most useful group of Ordovician to Devonian fossils. Of the significant trends, the reduction in the number of branches in a single colony seems to be of considerable importance. The earliest Late Cambrian and Lower Ordovician colonies had 40 or more separate branches (Fig. 22) but through time, most groups possessed fewer branches and the Silurian-Devonian important forms had only a single branch (Fig. 22). There is also a general trend in reversal of direction of growth relative to the initial cup so that Ordovician types grew down and Silurian forms grew up (Fig. 22). The shape of the cups, and the wall structure are additional features whose evolution can be traced in considerable detail.

CONODONTS

Another group of fossils whose precise biologic relationships remain a mystery is the conodonts. This group includes microscopic-sized elements which are cone-like, and comb-like but generally unlike anything living today (Fig. 3). Several thousand different types have been described from rocks ranging in age from Middle Cambrian to Late Triassic. They are abundant and widespread; different kinds seem to characterize each different age rock so that their value as index fossils is not excelled by any other group.

Conodonts are composed of calcium-phosphate and, though microscopic, are readily recovered from acid residues of limestones and shales. Certain types occur together as sinistral and dextral pairs. Other types are bilaterally symmetrical. In addition, certain assemblages showing patterns of pairs have been discovered suggesting that the individual conodont element was part of some bilaterally symmetrical soft bodied animal. Whether they are parts of worms, cephalopods, snails or fish or are the only remains of an extinct group, has not been determined. No living animal bears elements which are very similar.

Study of their mode of growth and development suggests that conodonts grew by secretion of layer upon layer and hence the outer most layer is the youngest. This consideration, along with the observation that broken parts are often regenerated suggests that conodonts were enclosed in some kind of fleshy medium during their life. Complete growth series are known and the life development as well as evolution is understood in some groups.

With all of these facts, no really satisfactory answer for their biologic relationship has been determined.

Conodonts bear a superficial resemblance to teeth and the terminology used to describe them is based on this illusion. Their widespread distribution suggests that they belonged to a free floating or swimming animal. All were marine.

PHYLUM BRACHIOPODA

The brachiopods constitute one of the most important groups of fossil invertebrates. The soft parts of these "clam-like" animals are enclosed by a shell which consists of two valves which are dissimilar in shape. The two valves are united at one end which is referred to as posterior. Most brachiopods lived semi-attached to some substratum by a large muscle which emerged from an opening at the posterior end. The valves at the anterior part of the shell could be opened for feeding and respiratory functions.

More than 15,000 species of fossil brachiopods have been described and approximately 200 species are living today. They are not common along the North American coasts. Because of this, the seasoned beachcomber may not be acquainted with their shell. Geologists and paleontologists, on the other hand, have encountered brachiopod shells in rocks from Precambrian to the Pleistocene and their general abundance has made them one of the best studied and most useful groups of fossils. They are clearly a "declining" race and have almost always been more abundant in the seas of the geologic past than they are today.

Brachiopods are generally small, one-half to three inches in greatest dimension. The two-valved shell is either calcareous or a mixture of calcareous and organic material which is readily preserved. The brachiopod animal consists of a body covered with a fleshy membrane which also secretes the shell. Food is taken by a lophophore, or arm-like structure, located in the anterior part of the shell. This structure bears numerous fine, hair-like cilia which can set up water currents and when the valves are separated, organic debris is removed from the water.

There are two important groups of brachiopods. The first includes primitive types whose shells are phosphatic and whose valves are held together by muscles without the aid of a well developed hinge structure (Fig. 23). This group is the Inarticulata. The second, more geologically important group, has shells which are largely calcite and whose valves have a distinct hinge area. These are the Articulata (Fig. 23). Living habits and soft parts of the two groups are quite distinct.

The shell form of brachiopods is diverse (Fig. 23). Robust, flat, triangular, elongate, wide and narrow shapes are known. Shells may be smooth or ornamented with coarse ribs and spines (Fig. 23).

Brachiopods have always been marine and largely attached. Evidently they could tolerate little change in normal marine salinity. One exception is the group of living inarticulates which can close their shell tightly and burrow into the bottom during periods of inhospitable ecologic conditions. Temperature tolerance is small in living groups which seem to prefer cool and temperate waters over tropical temperatures.

WORMS AND TRACE FOSSILS

Even worms, the majority of which have no hard parts, have left a record in the rocks of the earth. Worm tubes, body impressions, and quite often the jaws of certain types are found in rocks ranging in age from Late Precambrian to the Recent. The worm jaws are commonly well-preserved but the impressions and tubes are extremely difficult to understand. Living types collectively called worms are actually so diverse in their structure that several distinct phyla are recognized by specialists. These separate classifications are not of great value to the paleontologist who must deal with preservable parts or traces of those parts.

Marine worms have been abundant since the Precambrian and if all had left some preservable part, they undoubtedly would constitute one of the most important groups of fossils. The occasional worm trail, impression and tube which have been preserved, are considered to be a curiosity to most students and, therefore, are more interesting than useful. Recent work suggests that valuable ecologic data may be had by serious study of these trails, burrows, and "curiosities" (Fig. 23).

Living worms are bilaterally symmetrical animals with a well-developed alimentary canal and nervous system. They crawl, burrow, or swim, and inhabit marine, non-marine and terrestrial environments.

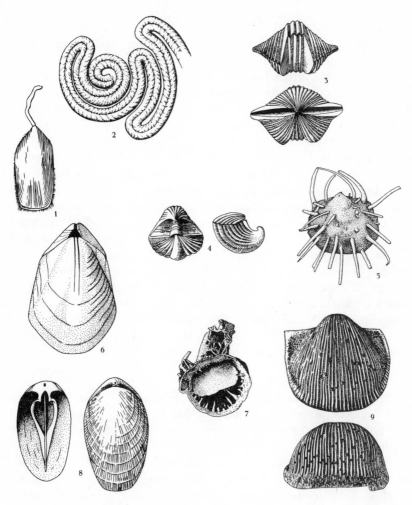

Figure 23. Brachiopods and trace fossils. 1. living inarticulate from Hawaiian Islands, **Lingula hawaiiensis** (X1); 2. a trace fossil (possible worm trail), **Taphrhelminthopsis auricularis,** Cenozoic of Italy (X.2); 3. tail end and beak views of articulate **Platystrophia acutilirata** (X1), a common fossil in Ordovician rocks of Midwestern United States; 4. beak and side views of **Cyrtina alpenensis,** articulate from the Devonian of Michigan (X1); 5. **Echinauris lateralis,** a Permian articulate with clasping spines (X4); 6. internal mold of **Pentamerus laevis,** a Silurian articulate from North America (X3); 7. an unusual articulate with coral-like shell, **Prorichthofenia permiana** from Permian of Texas (X1); 8. interior of one valve and exterior view of articulate **Rensselaeria marylandica,** Devonian of Maryland (X1); 9. top and end views of **Labriproductus worthensis,** a Mississippian articulate from Missouri (X2) (1, after Moore, Lalicker, and Fischer; 2, adapted from Hass et al.; 3, 2, 6, 8, after Easton; 5, 7, 9, adapted from Muir-Wood and Cooper).

PHYLUM MOLLUSCA

Snails, clams and cephalopods are three principal members of this important group. Most molluscs have a calcareous shell and those which lack this external armor are considered specialized. In addition to the three major groups, there are several other groups whose biologic interest is far greater than their geologic importance. This category includes the chitons, the monoplacophorans and scaphopods.

Most molluscs live in a marine environment and fossil types confirm that this has been the pattern of the past. There are many fresh water types and terrestrial air-breathing snails are common. The range of environments is rounded out by certain squids known today which can "fly" 150 feet through the air.

The earliest molluscs appear in the Cambrian and the group has continued as one of the most important groups of invertebrates to the present time. More than 125,000 species of molluscs have been described, of which approximately 80,000 are living. Collectively, the Phylum Mollusca ranks second only to the Arthropoda (insects and their kin) in numbers of species. Some 10 percent of all known invertebrates, fossil and Recent, are molluscs and during parts of the geologic past, particularly the Late Mesozoic and Cenozoic, molluscs were the dominant large invertebrates.

The Monoplacophorans and Mollusc Beginnings

Because living molluscs are either bilaterally symmetrical or have some trace of bilateral symmetry, it has long been assumed that the ancestral type for the entire group should also be bilaterally symmetrical.

Interesting fossil types such as the genus *Pilina* (Fig. 24) and its relatives have been known from rocks of Early Paleozoic age for years but these fossil shells which show some indication of bilateral symmetry do not reveal the biology of the animal which inhabited them.

In the 1950's, oceanographic vessels, dredging at depths of 11,000 to 19,000 feet in the Pacific off South America, recovered specimens so similar to the fossil *Pilina* that the name *Neopilina* was given to them. Most significant, however, was the determination of bilateral symmetry in the soft parts of the living species which showed relationship to certain types of annelid worms as well as to the molluscs. This "missing link" confirmed bilateral symmetry in a "primitive" molluscan type. Because of these important, yet primitive, characteristics, the group of monoplacophorans have been described as "living fossils" and the evolution of the molluscs, only guessed at previously, is now much better understood.

Figure 24. Ancestral molluscs and gastropod types. 1. **Pilina,** a Silurian monoplacophoran, internal view and external view of valves. Notice symmetrical arrangement of muscle scars in internal valve, Silurian, Europe (X.7), a cap-shaped gastropod, **Palaeoscurria calyptrata,** Silurian of Bohemia, upper and side views (X2.7); 3. shell of living gastropod **Buccinum undatum** (X1), showing relationship of body to shell orientation (after Knight et al.).

Class Gastropoda

Gastropods, or snails as they are commonly called, are univalved molluscs whose shell may be cap-like, coiled, or tubular (Fig. 25). The spiral coiling type is most common but one extinct group was coiled in one plane (planispiral) and there are fossil and living types with only traces of coiling preserved (the patellids, limpets, abalones, etc.,) (Fig. 25). Living gastropods have asymmetrical body structure and observation of the ontogeny of many species has convinced specialists that an evolutionary developmental pattern of twisting from an original symmetrical condition did take place.

The animal has a distinct head and a heavy muscular foot (Fig. 24). The anus, gills, mouth, etc., of necessity, are concentrated at the opening of the shell and hence the alimentary canal forms a loop. If bilaterally symmetrical forms are ancestral types, then during the evolution of the group, the foot, essential for effective locomotion, expanded

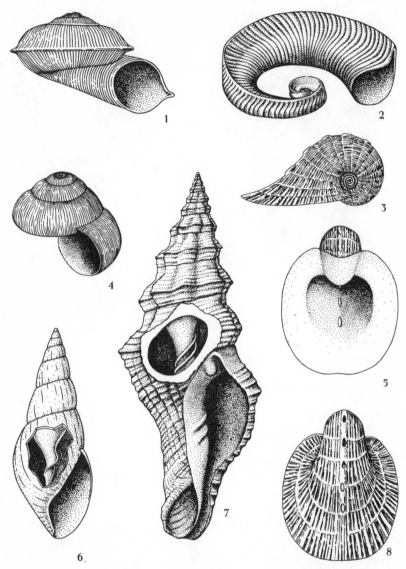

Figure 25. Gastropods. 1. low-coiling type, **Pleuromphalus seductor,** Silurian of Bohemia (X1.3); 2. loosely coiled type, **Ecculiomphalus alatus,** oblique view, Ordovician of Europe (X3/4); 3, 5, 8. planispiral variety, **Tremanotus alpheus,** side, inner, and upper views of a gastropod showing change in growth at maturity, Silurian, New York (X.5); 4. **Straparollus** sp., common Carboniferous type (X3/4); 6. **Soleniscus typicus,** a high spired type with opening to show central axis, Pennsylvanian, Illinois (X1); 7. a high spired gastropod with opening to show internal axis, **Latirus lynchis,** Miocene, France, approximately natural size (after Knight et al.).

and interfered with the anus and gills which were originally at the aperture of the shell. These systems were forced to one side in order to be above the foot and still have access to the opening of the shell. The change in growth pattern resulted in a distinct twisting and symmetry loss and certain soft structures, paired in primitive forms, are in living types represented by a single organ.

The nervous system is well developed and tentacles, eyes, etc., are present. The gills are specialized and the classification of living gastropods is based, in part, on their structure. Gastropods may be separately sexed or bisexual and some evidently give "live birth" to their young.

The shell consists of a spire (all volutions above the body chamber) and body chamber (last complete volution). The shells are commonly ornamented with ridges, nodes, spines, etc., and they may be low or high coiled or show no coiling at all (Figs. 24 and 25).

Gastropods are the only mollusc group to have attained a terrestrial habitat. The majority of snails, however, are marine or fresh water and live at depths of less than 200 feet. Most are active swimmers, crawlers, or drifters and only a few are sessile. They are either herbivores or carnivores and certain types are particularly fond of oysters.

The earliest gastropods are Cambrian types including low spiraled and planispiral forms (Fig. 25). Preservation in Paleozoic types is almost always as internal molds and very few details can be determined from such fossil forms. Highly ornamented shells were present in the Upper Paleozoic and many "Paleozoic types" are living today. Mesozoic and Cenozoic gastropods are commonly better preserved than their Paleozoic counterparts.

Class Cephalopoda

The squids, octopuses, cuttlefish, argonauts and pearly *Nautilus* are the living representatives of a molluscan class which also includes a host of extinct forms which have lived in abundance since the Upper Cambrian. The six hundred living species are considerably different from the fossil ancestors whose greater numbers suggest that cephalopods found life more comfortable in the geologic past. Cephalopods have always been marine organisms and most representatives of the group have been agile, active swimmers with a carniverous diet. Living cephalopods are so active and shy that their study has been very difficult and until recently little has been known about their habits and habitats. *Nautilus* is the only living cephalopod which carries its chambered shell externally (Fig. 26); most other living types are naked although a few have a small internal shell. Most fossil types were similar to *Nautilus* in shell bearing habit.

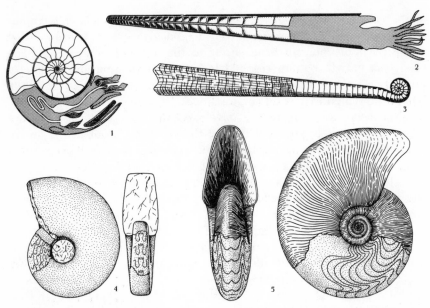

Figure 26. Cephalopods. 1. Cross section of hypothetical fossil cephalopod with body parts, based on analogy with living **Nautilus;** 2. reconstruction of section of straight nautiloid showing chambers and soft parts, 3. an Ordovician straight nautiloid from the Baltic, **Lituites litmus** (X.3); 4. **Prouddenites primus,** lateral and end view of a Pennsylvanian ammonoid; shell removed to show suture (X1.5); 5. typical Devonian ammonoid, **Manticoceras** sp., with shell and suture, an end and lateral view, approximately natural size. (1, 4, 5, after Arkel et al.; 2, 3, after Moore, Laliker and Fischer).

The shell of both living and fossil types of *Nautilus* and its relatives is univalved and internally partitioned. The internal walls form a series of chambers and the chambered part of the shell is called the phragmocone (Fig. 26). The final chamber, open at one end, housed the soft parts of the animal (Fig. 26). The living *Nautilus* has a distinct head with large well-developed eyes and tentacles which surround its mouth (Fig. 26). A mantle surrounds the body portion and water taken into the mantle is forcefully ejected through a structure which produces a jet propulsion of sorts for swimming. The only connection between the mantle cavity and the phragmocone is through the siphuncle, a tube-like structure which extends through all of the chambers to the initially formed chamber or protoconch (Figs. 26 and 27). Gas or liquid stored in the chambers for some buoyant factor was often balanced by the deposition of $CaCO_3$ in the chambers. The pattern formed by contact of the chamber wall with the outer wall of the animal's shell is called the suture line. Such configurations are commonly exposed in fossil forms when the outer shell surface has been removed (Fig. 27). Many fossils are preserved as internal molds and only the suture line remains.

The internal siphuncle and the configuration of the suture line are important in the classification of fossil cephalopods. One group, including the modern *Nautilus* which possesses relatively simple suture configurations and highly variable siphuncles, is called the nautiloids (Fig. 26). Another group, which ranged from the Middle Paleozoic to the end of the Mesozoic and had elaborate suture lines and a fairly uniform siphuncle pattern, is called the ammonoids (Fig. 27).

The earliest and most primitive cephalopods are superficially similar to the modern *Nautilus*. Other early forms had a straight shell

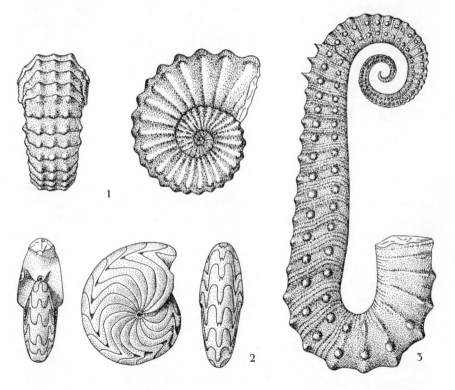

Figure 27. Ammonoid cephalopods. 1. advanced type with ribs and spines, suture not shown, **Acanthoceras rhotomagense,** Cretaceous, France (X1/3); 2. end and lateral views of **Imitoceras rotatorium,** outer shell removed to show suture (X1), Mississippian, Indiana; 3. an unusually coiled Cretaceous form, France, **Ancyloceras matheronianum** (X.2) (1, 2, after Arkel et al.; 3. adapted from d'Orbigny).

and some were more than 15 feet long, exclusive of soft parts. Early in the history of the cephalopods, the shell began to coil and after their appearance coiled types dominated the others. The nautiloids decreased in number after the Ordovician but one specialized group gave rise to the ammonoids which were the really successful cephalopods of the late Paleozoic and Mesozoic. This latter group, extinct since the Mesozoic, was large and diverse and rapidly evolving through time. Their shells are among the finest of the biostratigraphic or index fossils. The classification of the ammonoid cephalopods of Paleozoic and Triassic times is on the basis of their suture. World-wide distribution in a relatively short period of geologic time characterizes the group. Jurassic and Cretaceous types are more elaborately ornamented with spines, ribs, and other features which are utilized in their classification. One interesting group attained unusual coiling patterns and became cane-like (Fig. 27). The extinction of the ammonoids, still a puzzle, is used to mark the end of the Mesozoic Era in marine rocks.

The squids, octopoids and other cephalopod types, largely without shells, have left a very poor geologic record but are known in Pennsylvanian rocks in Illinois and Cenozoic rocks in several parts of the world.

Class Pelecypoda

The pelecypods or clams have a shell consisting of two valves. The valves are hinged on the dorsal side of the animal and hence a left and right side are produced. Shell structure in this group is diverse and, unfortunately for the paleontologist, seems to reflect the animal's environment to a greater degree than it does its kinship to other kinds. Hence, burrowers are commonly elongate and smooth, sessile forms are normally scabious, and free swimming types are more symmetrical. It is difficult to relate such diverse types in understandable lineages and most shells give only a hint of the former soft-bodied animal which inhabited them. A majority of fossil pelecypods, as well as those living today, were shallow marine types but fresh water varieties are also abundant.

The body is laterally compressed in the enclosed shell. Respiration is by means of gills. The foot of the clam is normally a large fleshy muscle which may be extended out of the shell for locomotion. The shell consists of $CaCO_3$ but in most clams it is a highly unstable $CaCO_3$ type which is not well-preserved. Because of this, many fossil pelecypods are molds and casts rather than original shell material. Such fossils are seldom ideal for serious study, and Mesozoic and older types are not nearly as well understood as other equally old fossils.

Modern species are classified according to the nature of their gills. Because only the shell is available for paleontologic study, the nature of the hingement between valves of the two shells has been used (Fig. 28) for classification.

One of the most important groups is the oysters and their kin. These were (and are) sedentary attached forms in which considerable modification of the shell has taken place. The left valve is the lower attached one and attachment is normally by cementation. The right valve may become a little lid-like structure. The oysters had their origin during the Permian and descendants were common during the Mesozoic and Cenozoic, as well as being abundant and of great economic importance today.

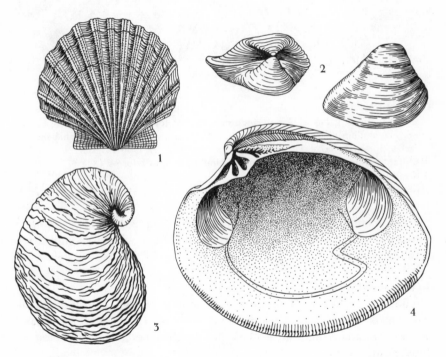

Figure 28. Pelecypods. 1. **Lyropecten madisonius,** a Miocene type from North America (X1/3); 2. two views of **Corbula undifera,** Cretaceous, Wyoming (X1); 3. a Cretaceous oyster-like shell, **Exogyra ponderosa** (X1/2), Texas; 4. internal view of a valve of **Venus mercenaria** (X1), Cenozoic and Recent, world wide. Notice muscle scars at either end of shell (adapted from Easton).

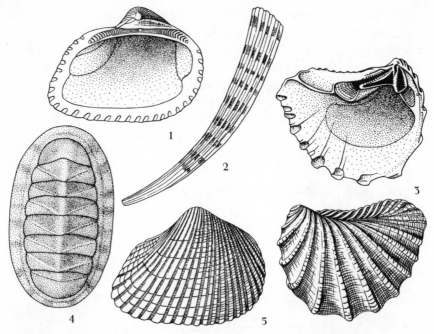

Figure 29. Pelecypods, scaphopods, and chitons. 1, 5. internal and external view of valve of **Arca ponderosa**, Recent form; 2. a modern scaphopod, **Dentalium elephantinum** (X.5); 3. a Cretaceous pelecypod, **Trigonia thoracica**, internal and external views of valves (X2/3), Gulf Coastal Plain; 4. **Chiton tuberculatus**, a Recent chiton similar to fossil forms (X1) (1, 3, 5, after Easton; 2, 3, Knight et al.).

The modern scallops include the *Pecten* (Fig. 28), a free-swimming type with heavy ribs on a symmetrical shell. This group extends back to the Ordovician.

Miscellaneous Mollusca

There are several less important molluscan types including the scaphopods, chitons and several extinct varieties (Fig. 29). Fossil types are not abundant and little geologic significance has been noted in these groups.

PHYLUM ECHINODERMATA

The animals which are classified together as echinoderms are outwardly different and one might suspect that there is little similarity between the stalked "sea lily" (crinoid) and the worm-like sea cucumber (holothurian). Yet all members of this diverse group possess marked similarity in basic structure. All have a primitive bilateral symmetry, often well developed during early embryonic growth but which, by maturity, is masked by a radial or "five-fold" symmetry. All have some kind of a water-vascular system which may combine functions of food gathering and locomotion with respiration. This system, with specialized internal structures and external plates, is the most distinctive feature of the phylum. Most, but not all, have an external armor of calcite plates.

There are two large ecologic categories of echinoderms; those which are primarily free moving and those which are primarily attached forms.

Free Living Types (Eleutherozoans)

ECHINOIDS

The sea urchin family includes hundreds of living types and an even greater number of fossil species. Many have their mouth on a flattened lower surface and their anus on the opposite or upper side. Living types have a shell with five double rows of plates which run from pole to pole (Fig. 30). This 20 plate arrangement is standard for living forms but the oldest fossil types are noteworthy because the number of plates was not standardized (Fig. 30). Through time, several groups of echinoids became flattened. Some extremely flattened sand dollar-types are primarily burrowers which feed on organic debris.

Paleozoic specimens are not common and echinoids have only been abundant since the Mesozoic. Most have been shallow water burrowers and vagrant types but reef dwelling varieties are common. Reduction in numbers of external plates and increase in complexity of these plates are two interesting evolutionary features of the group (Fig. 30).

STELLEROIDS

The starfishes and their kin have been living in the oceans for more than 400 million years. There are two principal types; the asteroids, or true starfishes, whose body and arms are not clearly separated (Fig. 30); and the ophiuroids, including the brittle stars, serpent stars, and basket stars, whose slender arms are more obviously differentiated from the body (Fig. 30). Fossil types are very similar to those living today. The individual elements of the starfish body are readily scattered after the death of the animal and disintegration of the muscles. Because of this, a whole fossil starfish is a rare fossil.

HOLOTHURIANS

The sea cucumbers have elongate "cucumber" shaped bodies and are different from other echinoderms because they possess no external

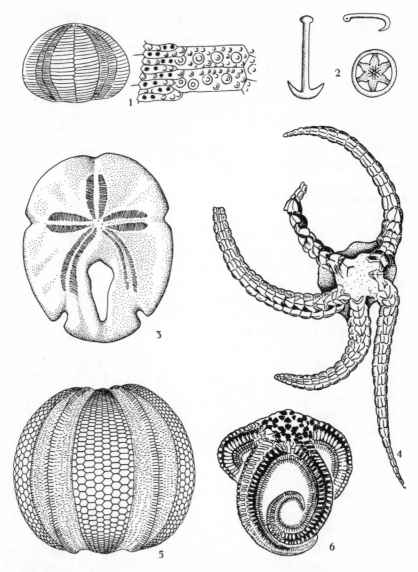

Figure 30. Echinoderms; echinoids, starfishes, and holothurians. 1. A small Cretaceous echinoid with enlargement of plates showing spine bases and pore openings (X.7); 2. holothurian sclerites, hook, anchor, and wheel (X180), Mesozoic and Cenozoic varieties; 3. a Pliocene sanddollar (echinoid), **Encope macrophora** (X1/2), South Carolina; 4. **Hallaster cylindricus,** an Ordovician ophiuroid from Canada (X.3); 5. Mississippian echinoid with numerous rows of plates, **Melonechinus multiporus,** Missouri (X1); 6. a Pennsylvanian starfish, **Calliasterella mira,** Russia (X1) (1, 2, 4-6, after Moore, Laliker and Fischer; 3, after Easton).

skeleton of plates but instead may have tiny calcite sclerites or spicules embedded in their flesh (Fig. 30).

All holothurians are marine. Some are burrowers, some crawlers or swimmers and all have a soft muscular body which is not readily preservable. The tiny sclerite particles are the principal item which has been preserved in rocks. More than one type of sclerite may be present in a single individual. The sclerites are shaped like many familiar objects; wheels, hooks, anchors, etc., only a few millimeters in diameter. These tiny microfossils are known to occur in rocks of Ordovician to Recent age.

Attached Types (Pelmatozoans)

CRINOIDS

Living attached echinoderms include approximately 800 species of crinoids whose greatest concentration is apparently the southwest Pacific-Indian Ocean area. A far greater number of sea lily species lived in the past, and recent evidence suggests that in the evolution of the group, many forms attained a free moving mode of life. The crinoid body consists of two main parts: A calyx, or globular shaped "head" which contains the visceral organs with arms which extend upward for food gathering, and a stem, or series of plates, which serve to hold the "head" or calyx above the sea floor (Fig. 31). There may be an attachment structure. The presence of a stem and the brilliant colors which may show in the membraneous covering of the calcareous plates has led to the present "sea lily" designation. Many living types are free-moving and some use their arms for rapid movement along the bottom.

As with most other echinoderms, the body area is covered with rows of plates. The arrangement of these plates has served as the basis for paleontologic classification. Crinoids lived from the Cambrian to the Recent but are most abundant in Ordovician and Mississippian rocks in North America. Some have considerable biostratigraphic value but well preserved calyxes are only locally abundant. Whole specimens with calyx and complete stem are extremely rare because more or less immediate disaggregation of the many plates occurs on death of the animal. The columnal plates of the stem are the chief constituent of many Paleozoic limestones.

PRIMITIVE ATTACHED FORMS

Attached types of echinoderms were more diversified and numerous during the early and middle Paleozoic than they are today. Extinct types include edriasteroids and their kin, cystoids and blastoids (Fig.

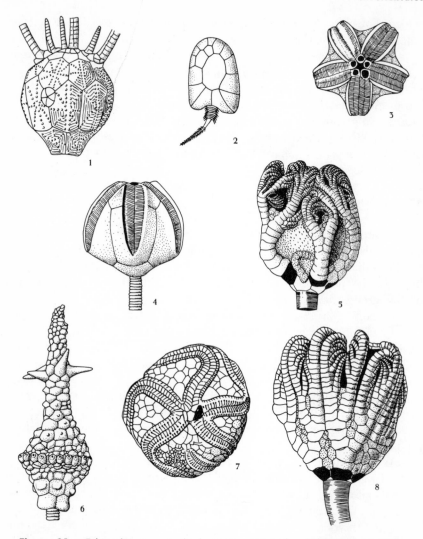

Figure 31. Echinoderms, attached types. Crinoids, blastoids, cystoids. 1. The cystoid **Hemicosmites pyriformis** from the Ordovician of Russia, approximately X1, note pore pattern on plates; 2. **Mitrocystites mitra,** a carpoid from the Ordovician of Bohemia, mouth at opposite end from "stem-like" appendage (X1); 3, 4. **Pentremites sulcatus,** a Mississippian blastoid in top view (3) and lateral view (4). Openings at top related to internal water system (X1); 5. Mississippian crinoid, **Onychocrinus ulrichi,** with arms folded over caylx, (X1); 6. crinoid with arms removed to show unusual calyx, **Uperocrinus nashvillae,** from Mississippian of Tennessee (X1); 7. Primitive echinoderm, **Edrioaster bigsbyi,** Ordovician of Canada (X1); 8. **Talanterocrinus** sp., a Pennsylvanian crinoid with arms rising from calyx (X1) (3, 4, adapted from Easton; others from Moore, Lalicker and Fischer).

31). Most of these types are so different from those living today that their biologic understanding is only partially satisfactory.

One primitive type had a symmetry which approached a bilateral condition, a tail-like appendage, and oral-aboral elongation and an arrangement of plates which has led some students to consider these as the possible ancestor of the vertebrates. Should this or another echinoderm-vertebrate transition be established, a major link in the chain of life will be understood. Other primitive types include a possible crinoid ancestor without true "arms", and box-like types which seem to have a starfish attached to one surface (Fig. 31). All of these types lived during the Paleozoic but were not common.

The cystoids and blastoids are similar to the crinoids, having a calyx mounted on a stem. These forms, extinct since the Permian, were specialized in number, size, arrangement and structure of the calyx plates. Cystoid's plates were perforated with a system of pores which was related to their internal water-vascular system (Fig. 31). The blastoids had a calyx which consisted of 13 rather regularly arranged plates on a short stem.

PHYLUM ARTHROPODA

This phylum includes the crabs, lobsters, insects and other living invertebrates which have segmented bodies and jointed limbs, as well as the extinct trilobites and eurypterids. The typical arthropod body is elongate and bilaterally symmetrical with vital organs enclosed in an organic or chitinoid skeleton. In many arthropods the skeleton is flexible, e.g. the shrimps, but in others, e.g. the lobsters and crabs, it is hard and brittle because of calcium carbonate shell. Those skeletons which have been impregnated with calcium carbonate have left the best fossils.

The group is enormously large. More than 700,000 species of insects are known and when this number is added to approximately 40,000 species of spiders and their kin, crustaceans, and millepedes, the total amounts to almost 80 percent of the one million living and fossil species of vertebrates and invertebrates. Geologically, the group is not as important as the present living numbers might suggest and except for the trilobites of the Paleozoic and small ostracode crustaceans, fossil arthropods are not common.

Arthropods have been highly successful in diverse habitats and range from the deep seas to high mountain latitudes. Some are aerial, some aquatic, and a great many are terrestrial. Geologically, the arthropods appear in the Cambrian (probably Precambrian) and have been rather numerous to the present day. If terrestrial and aerial types were more readily preserved we would probably find that arthropods have been among the most numerous invertebrates since the Middle Paleozoic. Our knowledge, however, rests primarily on marine types.

Primitive forms which may be arthropods or their immediate ancestors have been found in Precambrian rocks of Australia. Other definite types are known in unusually well-preserved conditions in Middle Cambrian shale of the Alberta-British Columbia Rockies.

Trilobites

The trilobites are one of the two most important groups of geologically significant arthropods. The group is characterized by the possession of a skeleton (carapace) which is divided into three lobes. The head, the thorax and the tail comprise the transverse segmentation but these structures (Fig. 32) are also lobed longitudinally. On the underside of the trilobite, biramous or double appendages existed in

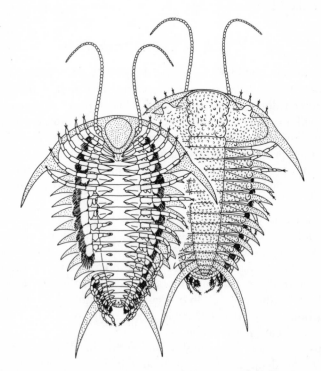

Figure 32. Lower (left) and upper (right) views of a trilobite showing appendages, antennae and external ornamentation. **Ceraurus pleurexanthemus,** Ordovician of New York (X2.1) (adapted from Harrington et al.).

life, a pair for each segment of the thorax (Fig. 32). The visceral organs are poorly known and inferences as to muscular, nervous, or respiratory systems or reproduction is based on information gained from study of living relatives. Trilobites were numerous during the Lower Paleozoic but were extinct by the end of that era.

The head bears structures which support compound eyes. The eye facets are commonly well-preserved and have been studied in detail. Prominent sutures run at various angles across the head and evidently were points for emergence of the body during molting of the skeleton. Molting is a common characteristic of arthropods and is necessary for these organisms because the shell does not grow as the animal grows. As the animal outgrows a previously formed carapace, he crawls out along fractures and secretes a new and larger carapace. Although all molting stages are known in only a few species of trilobites, it would appear that up to 27 molting stages was not unusual.

Trilobites were rapidly evolving forms and are of widespread use in biostratigraphic studies. Trilobite carapaces are probably the most valuable index fossil of the Cambrian, becoming less important in Late Paleozoic rocks before their extinction (Fig. 33).

Most trilobites were mud eaters, taking in large quantities of mud and debris, removing the organic part and passing off the indigestible portion. Little is known of the appendages but the depressed flat shape and dorsally placed eyes further suggest a mode of life of crawling or swimming along the bottom.

Certain types, early in the history of the trilobites, lost functional eyes (Fig. 33). Whether these forms lived in very deep water below the zone of light penetration or if other sensory organs, not preserved, served the function of light perception, is unknown.

Ostracodes

The second most important group of geologically significant arthropods are the ostracodes. In contrast to the trilobites, ostracodes are abundant today and study of living types has enhanced our knowledge of the fossils (Fig. 34).

Ostracodes are small animals, most of which have a two valved shell. The body is never preserved but numerous shells, only a millimeter or so in size, have been found in rocks ranging from the Cambrian to the Recent. They are abundant in marine and fresh water areas today and one terrestrial species is known. Living ostracodes molt periodically and up to nine molting stages have been noted.

Both swimming and bottom dwelling types are known but the majority today, as in the past, were evidently adapted for a bottom dwelling existence. The shell types evolved rapidly and many are im-

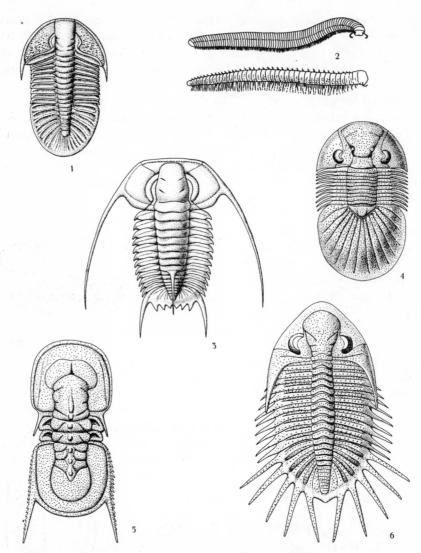

Figure 33. Arthropods. 1. **Orria elegans,** a trilobite from the Cambrian of Utah, well defined head but thorax and tail less distinctly separated (X.5); 2. upper, **Iulus** sp. a living millepede compared with **Euphoberia** sp. a fossil millepede from the Pennsylvanian of Illinois, both approximately X1; 3. **Pseudokainella keideli,** an Ordovician trilobite with long spines and median spine in central lobe (X6); 4. **Scutellum costatum,** a Devonian trilobite illustrating eye bases, small thorax and large tail (X.5), Germany; 5. **Pleuroctenium granulatum,** a Cambrian trilobite without eyes showing more or less equal sized tail and head and small thorax (X4.5); 6. **Asteropyge punctata,** with large spinose tail, Devonian of Germany (X1.5) (2, from Moore, Lalicker and Fischer; others from Harrington et al.).

portant geologic tools for age determination. In addition, today many are restricted to rather narrow ecologic niches, preferring water with certain pH, temperature, current, or sediment. These have proven of great value in the interpretation of environments of the geologic past.

Insects and Eurypterids

Of less direct geologic importance but of considerable biologic significance are the spiders, insects, (Fig. 34) and a variety of living and

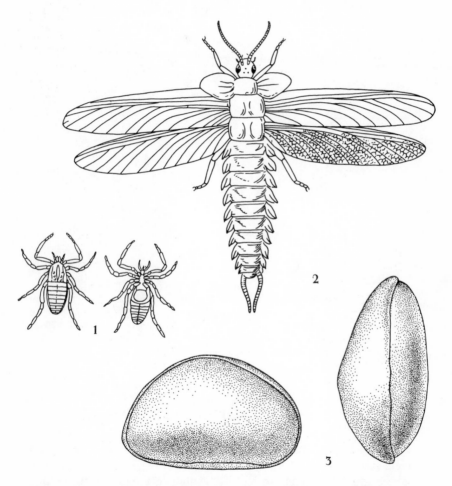

Figure 34. Miscellaneous arthropods. 1. Spider, **Plesiosiro madeleyi,** Pennsylvania, Europe (X1); 2. Winged insect, **Stenodictya lobata,** Pennsylvanian, France (X1); 3. ostracodes **Ovovytheridea nuda,** lateral and end views, Cretaceous, Africa (X60). (1, 2, from Moore, Lalicker and Fischer; 3, adapted from Benson et al.).

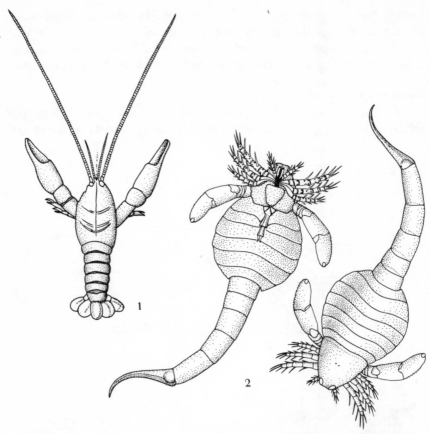

Figure 35. Eurypterids and lobsters. 1. **Eryma leptodactylina,** a lobster from the Jurassic of Germany (X1); 2. dorsal and ventral views of the eurypterid, **Carcinosoma scorpionis,** from the Silurian of New York. These sea scorpions included some of the largest invertebrates which have ever lived (X.13) (1, after Moore, Lalicker and Fischer; 2, after Størmer et al.).

extinct arthropods including the eurypterids (Fig. 35). The eurypterids, or sea scorpians, were both small and large-sized arthropods which inhabited brackish water areas of the Paleozoic. Their restricted environmental range has made them of only secondary importance in geologic studies.

Insects, spiders, etc., have left a poor geologic record. One remarkable insect with a wing span of 29 inches is known from the Pennsylvanian (Fig. 34). Insects must be considered of great geologic importance for their work in fertilization and spreading of pollen for plants.

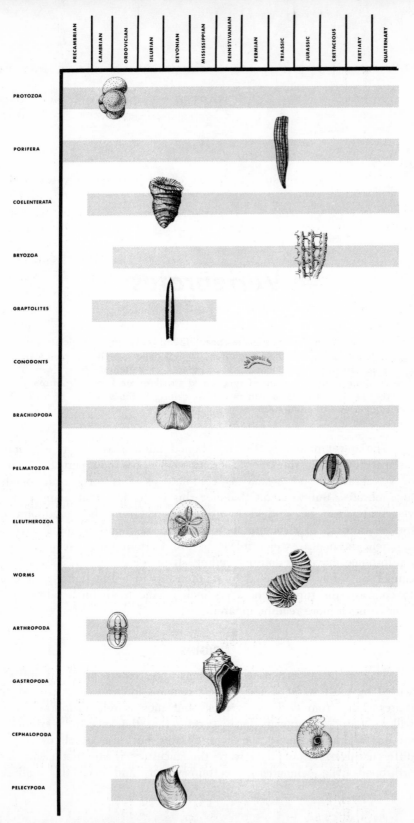

CHART 2. Development of the invertebrates and their distribution through time.

8

Vertebrates

Vertebrate animals have been found only in Ordovician and younger rocks, but their evolution from fish-like animals to mammals is remarkably well understood. Sequences of vertebrate fossils which illustrate the relationship of function to structure are known from many continents and there remain few missing links in the evolution of major categories of vertebrates.

The development of the backboned animals is one of the most fascinating parts of the story of evolution. For the most part, the record of vertebrates is not nearly as complete as it is for certain of the invertebrates. But to counterbalance this is the fact that many extinct vertebrates can be studied and understood from the standpoint of the relationship of structure to function; a relationship not always so apparent in many extinct invertebrates. Certain extinct cephalopods, for instance, have an unusual coiling shape (Fig. 27), a shape which cannot be safely interpreted in relationship to a functional character. In contrast, the function of a six inch canine tooth on a sabre tooth tiger is much more readily apparent.

ORIGINS

The origin of vertebrates and their ancestry are problems still obscured by too few facts. The earliest remains interpreted as true vertebrates come from Ordovician rocks but most surely Cambrian types will be found. It appears fairly certain that the ancestral vertebrates are to be found among the invertebrates but just which of several different invertebrate phyla were the ancestors is still not clear. The arthropods, the echinoderms, certain worms and even the molluscs have been seriously considered as vertebrate ancestors. Specialized internal structures, bilateral symmetry, etc. are the features which must be considered important for morphologic comparisons.

There is some evidence that points to an unusual group of echinoderms as possible vertebrate ancestors, and it is hoped that additional data will be made available in the near future which will aid in this understanding. Primitive vertebrates have a symmetry, and a developmental pattern very similar to certain echinoderms and if the internal organization can be further substantiated, serious consideration will have to be given to this theory. Geologically, echinoderms appeared in the Cambrian and so, theoretically, could have been the vertebrate ancestors.

STRUCTURAL ORGANIZATION OF THE VERTEBRATES

The vertebrates are the most important members of the Phylum Chordata which includes animals having an internal support, a notochord or a vertebrate structure. Specialists have emphasized that the long axis of the body is horizontal in typical vertebrates and that any departure from this position is a form of specialization.

CLASSIFICATION

There are five large categories of vertebrates: fishes, amphibians, reptiles, birds and mammals. All except mammals are commonly designated as "lower" vertebrates. The record of the evolution of these groups is good, and relationships between major categories are apparent. Only the birds and mammals have not given rise to "higher" groups of vertebrates. The Early and Middle Paleozoic can be regarded as the Age of Fishes, the Upper Paleozoic-Mesozoic, the Age of Reptiles, and the Cenozoic, the Age of Mammals. All five major groups of vertebrates have living representatives although the amphibians and reptiles have been declining groups for millions of years. The major groups of vertebrates appeared at intervals of 50-150 million years but it has been 170 million years since the appearance of the first mammals and this group has not yet given rise to a new group. Has the evolution of major kinds of vertebrates stopped?

One interesting observation is concerned with the appearance of giants in each of the major groups of vertebrates. This trend toward larger and larger forms has been repeated in each of the groups although to different degrees. For instance, from the Devonian to the Pennsylvanian, amphibians increased in size by a factor of six, but in a similar length of time (Permian-Jurassic) reptiles increased 54 times in size. Mammals show the trend best and from four-inch Jurassic types to 100 foot whales, an increase of 300 times has taken place.

FISHES

There were four major types of fishes living by the end of the Devonian and all except one are represented in the fish faunas of today.

Agnatha

The agnathids or jawless fish are evidently the most primitive and were the first vertebrates to appear. Most of the Paleozoic types were heavily armored and are called ostracoderms. All of the armored types were extinct by the end of the Paleozoic and only the lamprey and its kin, most likely primitive agnathids, have survived to the present. In contrast to the armored types, the living agnathids have a smooth body, a primitive fin development, and a predaceous to parasitic mode of life. Both modern types and fossil forms lacked true jaws, a fact of considerable importance.

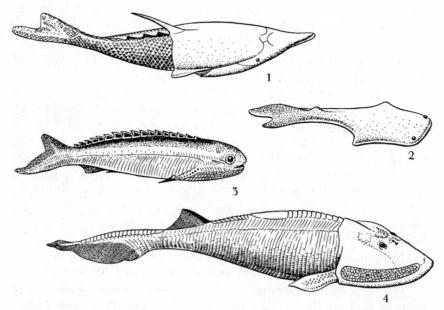

Figure 36. Ostracoderms of the Lower Paleozoic. 1. **Pteraspis;** 2. **Thelodus;** 3. **Pterolopis;** 4. **Hemicyclaspis.** Most ostracoderms had heavy head shields and scales behind, but variation from this "norm" is indicated. All approximately 1/2 natural size. (after Colbert).

Many ostracoderms were small and flattened. Their dorsally placed eyes and tail structure suggest that life was spent primarily as bottom-dwellers rather than as active swimmers (Fig. 36). A few were lightly armored and perhaps more active. Certain types had elaborate head shields with specialized structures which have been interpreted as electric sensory areas (Fig. 36).

The Ordovician ostracoderms were common in certain fresh and brackish water environments in several parts of the world but marine types have also´ been identified. These early forms were very similar to certain echinoderms in placement of body "armor", size and symmetry.

Placoderms

The absence of jaws limited the ostracoderms to a rather narrow environmental range. Their nourishment depended upon mud-sucking, and they digested available organic particles from the muddy, aquatic bottoms. By progressive modification of certain gill arches, a working jaw structure evolved and at this level of evolution these fishes, some still ostracoderm-like, are called placoderms.

The progressive development of jaws from the primitive gill arch apparatus is clearly evidenced by the nerve arrangement, and by certain embryologic changes observed in living types. Fossil forms provide additional evidence of this development. The appearance of jaws was a major advancement for vertebrates and allowed them many new environmental niches and a greater variety of food (including each other).

Placoderms were a large and varied Paleozoic group, and like their agnathid ancestors, inhabited fresh and marine water environments (Fig. 37). Enormous marine placoderms were the largest vertebrates of their time. Several groups of placoderms are known. Some are very shark-like and the ancestors of the sharks are probably within this group. Placoderms were widespread but success, measured in the eons of geologic time, was short-lived and all were extinct by the end of the Paleozoic.

Sharks

This large and successful group probably descended from the placoderms but has many structural features which distinguishes it from the other fishes. Most distinctive of these differences is a skeleton of cartilage, not bone. Cartilage is not readily preserved; therefore a calcified brain case, rare body impressions, or more commonly, teeth are about the only part of sharks preserved for paleontologic study. General body shape has changed little since their appearance in the

Devonian and a predaceous mode of life has probably always characterized the group (Fig. 37).

Living types are marine but a fresh water group lived during the Paleozoic. With this outstanding exception, the sharks appear to have been a rather uniform group from their first appearance to the present day.

Figure 37. Placoderms and sharks. 1. **Bothriolepis,** a Devonian placoderm; and 2. **Cladoselache,** a Devonian shark. (approximately 1/3 natural size) (after Colbert).

Bony Fishes (Osteichthyes)

The bony fishes, including most of the types familiar to the sportsman, are the "true" fishes and they have continued to increase in kinds and numbers from the Devonian to the Recent. The earliest forms were evidently fresh water types whose descendants inhabited the Paleozoic lakes and seas in tremendous numbers. More than 30,000 species are known today.

The earliest bony fish were small forms with thick scales, large eyes, and fins, some of which had bony spines. This primitive type was almost extinct by the end of the Paleozoic although a few types survive today.

The exact ancestor is unknown. By the end of the Paleozoic, several advanced groups appeared which were the dominant Mesozoic types. These had a more advanced jaw and were generally larger than their Paleozoic ancestors. Characteristics of these were transitional to those of the most advanced group which appeared in the Jurassic and which includes 99 percent of living fish. Many structural modifications can be noted in the advanced forms and scale evolution, tail modification and jaw development are only a few of the well documented evolutionary features. Diversity in modern types ranges from one-half inch to 40 foot varieties.

With all of this success, however, one group of bony fish has been of considerable more importance to the evolution of the vertebrates than the living types. This is the lobe finned fish, the immediate ancestral group of the other vertebrates (Fig. 38).

The lobe finned fishes appeared in the Devonian. They had an air sac connected to the throat, a feature present in all bony fish and also internal nostrils. This feature, and its relationship to the lungs, is a fascinating part of vertebrate evolution. It is assumed that the primitive air sac had an unstable position on the throat of the fish, unfavorable if it were to be utilized for air breathing. Through time, the position, and stability, changed. In modern bony fish, the sac is used as a hydrostatic organ, not for breathing. The lobe finned fish perfected and modified the air sac for a breathing apparatus. There are three different air breathing fish today, curiously limited to the southern hemisphere. These forms, "living fossils" similar to representatives of a Devonian group which gave rise to land vertebrates, give us many clues to the past (Fig. 38). In addition to functional lungs, two of the types have big fleshy lobes which enable them to walk. Devonian types are similarly built. Two living types can burrow into stream banks and live out of water for several months. The Devonian types perfected this and by the time of the Late Devonian-Early Mississippian were so well adapted to spending part of their life out of water that they are called Amphibians.

AMPHIBIANS

From an impartial evolutionary viewpoint, the amphibians can be regarded as important principally as the transition between the fish and the reptiles. They were never as abundant nor have they been as geologically useful as their ancestors or descendants.

Problems of life on land included that of breathing air, of skin drying, of maneuvering their bulk under the full force of gravity with no

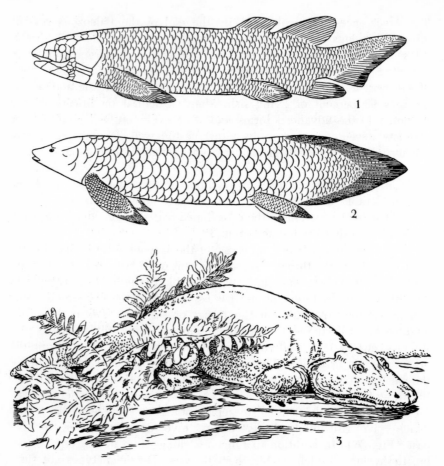

Figure 38. Lungfishes and amphibians. 1: **Dipterus,** Devonian lungfish, approximately 1/4 natural size; 2. **Epiceratodus,** Australian lungfish living today, some up to five feet in length; 3. **Eryops,** one of the largest amphibians reached six feet or so in length, Permian, Texas (after Colbert).

water buoyancy, of reproduction and locomotion. Vertebrate specialists maintain that breathing was no problem but that the skin drying problem and locomotion were only partially solved by the amphibians and that the reproduction problem was never solved. Paleozoic amphibians, as well as those living today, were forced to return to the water to lay their eggs in the protective and nourishing aquatic environment. Even with such problems, however, the transition to land was made. The range of environmental niches made available by this change led to the real success of the vertebrates.

There were several important groups of Paleozoic amphibians, some of which attained lengths of six feet or so. Most were bulky, rather awkward types and the largest types had a weak vertebral column and probably spent most of their time in water (Fig. 38). Several different vertebral types have been noted on fossil specimens and this probably represents evolutionary attempts at solving the new "out of water" gravity problem. Many families evolved during the Devonian-Triassic interval, after which most types became extinct. Only a few (toads, frogs, salamanders, etc.) survived to the Recent.

REPTILES

The water-to-land adaptive gap was bridged by the amphibians and within a few million years of their appearance, the first reptiles evolved. The transition between amphibians and reptiles is so complete that the leading American specialists cannot agree whether certain forms should be classified as advanced reptile-like amphibians or primitive amphibian-like reptiles. The transition was made during the Pennsylvanian Age and Permian reptiles were successfully competing with their amphibian ancestors. Perhaps the most important difference between these primitive reptiles and their amphibian ancestors was the ability of the reptiles to lay an amniote egg. This egg, with durable calcareous covering and a rich glob of enclosed nutrient, freed the vertebrates from their cyclic return to water. The reproductive process was now completed on land. There are other preservable morphologic differences of importance including modifications of the skull, back-bone, shoulder bones, ribs and feet.

The earliest reptiles ranged from approximately one foot to eight feet. Some were plant eaters, but a few were equipped with a complement of teeth which suggest definite carnivorous habits.

Reptiles evolved rapidly in the terrestrial environments and during the Permian and Triassic they were the most abundant and widespread land vertebrates. Several different reptilian groups acquired mammal-like characters during this interval. Which group or groups was the immediate ancestors of the mammals is not clear.

In addition to the advanced reptiles, many other types evolved during the Mesozoic and give firm support to the idea that this was the age of the reptiles (Fig. 39).

Dinosaurs

Probably the most spectacular Mesozoic reptiles were the dinosaurs. It has been emphasized by vertebrate specialists that most dinosaurs

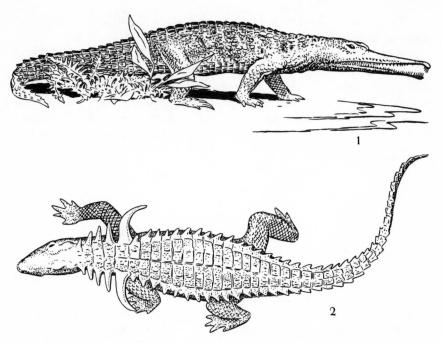

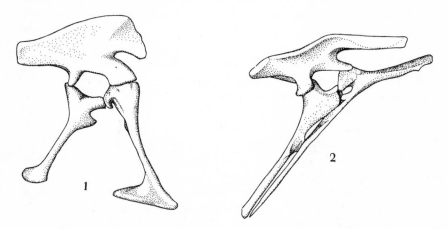

Figure 39. Triassic reptiles. 1. **Rutiodon,** reptile which lived in streams and lakes; 2. **Desmatosuchus,** an armored form with heavy plates and spines. Both attained lengths of 10 feet or more (after Colbert).

Figure 40. Pelvis structure in dinosaurs. 1. saurischian tri-radiate type, pubis extending forward and down, ischium extending backward and down, under the ilium; 2. ornithischian tetra-radiate pelvis, pubis extending upward and backward, ischium in same position as in saurischian, and ilium with forward component of growth above (after Romer).

were vegetarians, and although they have the reputation of being terrible, the name dinosaur (terrible lizard) is a misnomer.

There were two large groups of dinosaurs, each characterized by a particular pelvic structure (Fig. 40). One, the Saurischia, had a "triradiate" structure with pubis bone extending down and forward beneath the ilium and adjacent to the ischium which extends backward and downward. The second group was characterized by a "tetraradiate" pelvic structure, so named because of a forward projecting pubis which also grew downward for another component of growth. The ilium and ischium had similar dimensions to those of the Saurischians. This group is called the Ornithischians.

SAURISCHIANS

There are two varieties of Saurischians: Theropods, the only flesh-eating dinosaurs, such as *Tyrannosaurus* and *Allosaurus* (Fig. 41); and the Sauropods, the largest land animals which have lived. They were vegetarians and primarily quadripedal. Two of these sauropods were *Diplodocus* and *Brontosaurus*.

Certain kinds were 70 to 80 feet in length and weighed 30 to 40 tons (Fig. 41). These large types were semi-aquatic at maturity, probably in order to adequately support such bulk. These were true giants and they illustrate several important points concerning dinosaur evolution. Given the proper environmental conditions, reptiles grew continually. Also, a large size helped in the maintenance of a uniform body temperature, a feature needed by reptiles. Large size has its disadvantages too, including the problem of protection from extremes of heat or cold. Also, a leg fracture which might only cripple a smaller animal is usually fatal for larger beasts.

Theropods and sauropods were common dinosaurs during the Jurassic and Cretaceous and then, along with most other reptilian types, became extinct.

ORNITHISCHIANS

The Ornithischians were a more diverse group in their evolution but none were as large or ferocious as their Saurischian cousins. Four distinct varieties of Ornithischians evolved during the Jurassic and Cretaceous and then became extinct. Their extinction has been used to mark the close of the Mesozoic Era of time.

Ornithopods: This was the primitive group and includes the duck-billed dinosaur and its kin (Fig. 42). Most types were bipedal and some had a remarkable skull modification including nasal passages which probably allowed storage of air while the animal ducked for

Figure 41. Flying reptiles and dinosaurs. 1. **Rhamphorhynchus,** a Jurassic flying reptile approximately two feet long; 2. **Allosaurus,** a 40 foot saurischian dinosaur of the Jurassic; 3. **Ornithomimus,** a six foot saurischian of the Cretaceous; 4. **Camarasaurus,** a 20 foot sauropod of the Jurassic (1-3, after Colbert; 4, after Romer).

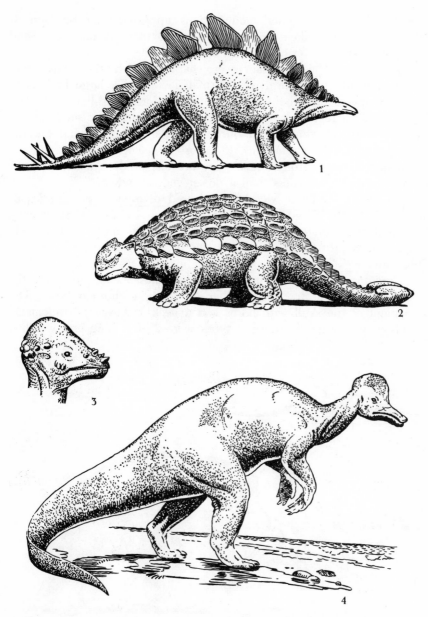

Figure 42. Ornithischian dinosaurs. 1. **Stegosaurus,** a 20 foot Jurassic vegetarian with bony plates on its back; 2. **Ankylosaurus,** also 20 feet or so in length with heavy body armor, Cretaceous; 3. **Pachycephalosaurus,** an ornithopod with a thick bony growth above the brain; 4. **Corythosaurus,** a 30 foot, semi-aquatic ornithopod with a skull modified for storage of air while the animal fed under water (after Colbert).

aquatic plant food. Other modifications appeared, the function of which escapes us today. One type had more than six inches of solid bone for a skull "battering ram" (Fig. 42).

Stegosaurs: These dinosaurs were characterized by the genus *Stegosaurus,* a quadrapedal form with a small head and a large body with a row or rows of long bony plates along the dorsal mid-line (Fig. 42). These were 20 feet in length and, in one way, the least successful of the dinosaurs. They appeared during the Early Jurassic and became extinct early in the Cretaceous, the shortest geologic range of any of the major dinosaur groups. Also, they are one of the smallest groups, only two families and less than a dozen genera known.

Ankylosaurs: These were the armored dinosaurs, the Cretaceous successors of the Stegosaurs. About the same size as the Stegosaurs, they had bony plates which must have covered most of the body (Fig. 42). Nearly twice as many types of Ankylosaurs are known as Stegosaurs.

Ceratopsians: The last major group of dinosaurs to appear are the Cretaceous *Triceratops,* and another dozen or so horned types. Development of the skull with horns and a neck-skirt was a "trademark" of this group (Fig. 43). Largest types were 25 feet long and weighed

2

Figure 43. Ceratopsian dinosaurs. 1. **Protoceratops,** ancestral ceratopsian and its eggs, known from abundant material found in Mongolia, about nine feet in length; 2. **Triceratops,** 25 foot Cretaceous dinosaur with well developed horns (after Colbert).

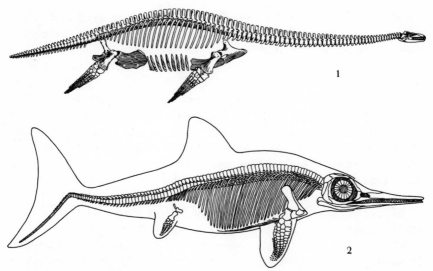

Figure 44. Swimming reptiles. 1. **Muraenosaurus,** 21 foot Jurassic plesiosaur; 2. **Ichthyosaurus,** 4-10 foot Mesozoic types, here showing body outline around skeleton (after Romer).

six or more tons. Great herds of ceratopsians ranged over North America
and numerous fossils have been collected. One dwarfed group including
eggs, has been discovered in Asia (Fig. 43). It appears that the ceratopsians were still expanding and numerous, when, for reasons still
unknown, they, along with the other dinosaurs and many types of
reptiles, became extinct.

SWIMMING REPTILES
     There were many kinds of reptiles which reverted to a mode of
life which had been abandoned by their ancestors. Most swimming
reptiles lived during the Mesozoic but a few (alligators and crocodiles)
have survived to the present. The *Ichthyosaurus* was a porpoise-type
streamlined for fast swimming and fish eating and ranging in size from
a foot to more than 10 feet (Fig. 44). They had long slender skulls,
an efficient set of fish-catching teeth, specialized eyes and well developed paddles for moving through the water. Hundreds of well-
preserved specimens have been excavated from Mesozoic rocks in
Germany and the United States. Specimens from Germany have delicate
impressions of the skin preserved with the bony skeleton. Other marine
types include the Plesiosaurs (Fig. 44) with long necks, short tails
and stout swimming paddles; the mosasaurs with short necks and long
tails, and other kinds of sea monsters which could justifiably serve as

models for sea monsters of legends. Most were short lived and extinct by the end of the Cretaceous. Their ecologic replacements in modern seas are the dolphin, porpoise and other whales.

Flying Reptiles

The multiple problems of flight were at least partially solved by the reptiles during the Jurassic. Several kinds of flying types evolved and were somewhat successful. They became extinct during the Cretaceous. Flying organisms seldom leave good fossil records and our knowledge of most is based on few specimens (Fig. 41). Most of the flying reptiles evidently lived in an area close to a marine environment where fish catching was a mode of life. Most had a length of a foot or so, but some kinds with a wing span of 20 feet have been found. Footprints, suspected to have been made by flying reptiles, have been found and it appears that they were extremely awkward on the ground. Questions of skin covering, metabolism rate, and flying capabilities with less than satisfactory wing structures, are unsolved problems of the flying reptiles.

BIRDS

The fourth large category of vertebrates has left a very poor geologic record. The first birds appeared in the Jurassic and marvelous details of feather preservation have permitted differentiation from the flying reptiles. The two flying groups probably evolved from the same reptilian stock. Jurassic and Cretaceous types had teeth, and although the geologic record is poor, it clearly indicates that this was a primitive condition lost in advanced Cenozoic forms. The anatomy of Cenozoic birds is quite uniform and external non-preservable characteristics are used in differentiating living species. Very few complete bird skeletons have been found and although knowledge of living species is far advanced, bird paleontology is less adequately understood.

EXTINCTION AND SURVIVAL

Of the groups of lower vertebrates, only the fish and the birds have continued to increase in number and kind since the Mesozoic Era. From more than a dozen major kinds of reptiles, numerous during the height of reptilian evolution in the Mesozoic, only four groups have survived.

Ultimately, any group of organisms will continue to survive if it is able to meet the successive environmental challenges. Atmospheric temperature change, disease, mass destruction, parasites, etc., are only a few of the environmental items which have been suggested as the cause of extinction at the end of the Mesozoic. In general, students have looked for a simple answer, a single process or event which might have caused the death of all the varied reptilian types. What could adequately explain the extinction of the ceratopsian dinosaurs has generally been untenable as a reason for the extinction of the swimming plesiosaurs, and vice-versa. Probably, the reasons for the reptilian extinctions are multiple. The operation of different processes which lead to extinction during a more or less penecontemporaneous time interval is the difficult problem to explain.

MAMMALS

At the height of the success of the reptiles, a small group of mammals appeared. Their ancestors were among the mammal-like reptiles of the Triassic but just which one or ones of the several such groups was the actual ancestral group is not certain. The earliest remains which are advanced enough to be considered mammals have been found in Lower Jurassic rocks. The fossils consist of teeth and jaws, a few bones and little more. The teeth are distinctive, however, and by themselves give a good indication of size, age, diet, and indirectly, the environment, of the animal which bore them. Of all the skeletal remains, teeth are by far the most important and instructive in the study of mammals. Unlike their reptilian ancestors, mammals had highly differentiated teeth, that is, incisors, canines, pre-molars and molars, a specialization which had no little role in their success. The skull and post-cranial skeleton are less important because most mammals, while differing in proportion as well as certain detail, have a remarkably uniform skeleton exclusive of the teeth.

There are, of course, many other differences between the mammals and the reptiles. Features of the brain, the skin, the ear structure, nasal structure, pelvis, jaw, and body temperature control, are only a few differences. Many of these things have not been preserved as fossils but the sturdy $CaPO_4$ teeth are readily preserved and have given most of the data that we have concerning many mammal types.

Primitive Types and the Marsupials

Mesozoic mammals were small and rodent-sized. Several tooth types have been described. The marsupials and their close relatives, the placentals, evolved from one of these groups during the late Mesozoic. The marsupials are more primitive in many respects but along with the aberrant monotremes (duck-billed platypus, spiney anteaters) have survived to the present.

The centers of marsupial evolution were in Australia and South America, where, because of geographic isolation, these animals were able to gain a foothold before their placental cousins. Competition with placental types hindered their development in South America but few placentals reached Australia before man brought them there and in this "secluded" environment, marsupials evolved much the same way as the placentals did in other parts of the world. Marsupial wolves, cats, rabbits, squirrels, bears, etc. evolved during the Cenozoic, and are very much like their placental counterparts which evolved on other continents. This is an excellent example of how similar environmental conditions can encourage similar morphologic adaptions. Such parallel evolution can be noted in other fossil groups but perhaps no other group illustrates the principle so well.

Placental Mammals — A Success Story

Approximately 95 percent of the mammals which lived during the Cenozoic were placentals. The placentals moved into the environmental niches vacated by the Mesozoic reptiles and filled these vacancies in a much bigger way than they had ever been filled before. Almost anything that the reptiles did — swim, fly, or bite each other — was done bigger and better by mammals. Flying mammals (bats) are better flyers than was the Pterodactyl. Swimming mammals (whales and kin) are at least the equal if not better swimmers than the *Ichthyosaur*. On land, mammals have developed more diverse habitats than their reptilian progenitors. Cenozoic mammals are so diverse and have left such a good record that their study is a separate subject. The classification of more than 2,600 fossil and living genera (with many times that number of species) is complex and most specialists would recognize at least 28 different orders. More than half this number of orders are living today. These 28 orders may be further grouped together and considered as representatives of four larger categories: the Unguiculates, Glires, Mutica and Ferungulates.

UNGUICULATES

This large category includes the insectivores (moles, hedgehogs, shrews), the bats, the anteaters, sloths, primates and several extinct types. These groups are diverse but certain tooth and structural features of the skeleton suggest that they had a common ancestor. It is considered the primitive group of mammals and appeared in the Cretaceous.

Some of the more interesting members of this group are the large ground sloth (Fig. 45) and the glyptodont which is an extinct relative of the armadillo (Fig. 45). These were heavy, massive animals, scavengers and vegetarians, and they lived in many parts of North and South America. Sloth remains found in caves in the southwest United States are associated with artifacts which suggest that they were contemporary with man.

The primates are unique mammals in terms of their mental development but in many structural features they show relationship to

Figure 45. Unguiculate mammals. 1. Giant ground sloth, some more than 12 feet high, Late Cenozoic; 2. heavily armored glyptodont, six feet or so in length (after Colbert).

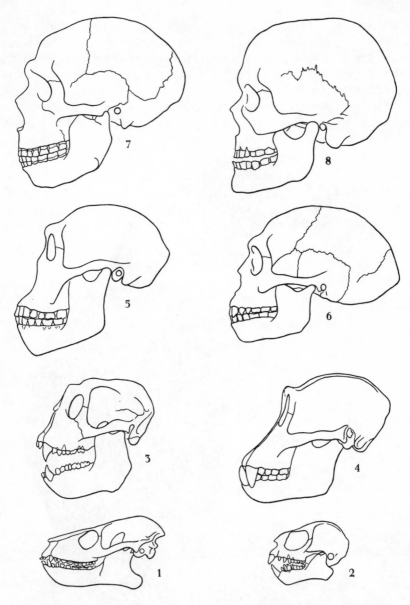

Figure 46. Primate skulls. 1. **Notharctus,** an Eocene lemur; 2. **Tetonius,** an Eocene tarsioid; 3. **Mesopithecus,** a Pliocene monkey-like primate; 4. **Pan,** modern chimpanzee; 5. **Australopithecus,** Pleistocene man-like primate; 6. **Pithecanthropus,** primitive Pleistocene man; 7. **Homo neanderthalensis,** Late Pleistocene man; 8. **Homo sapiens,** Cro-magnon man. 1-3, approximately one-half natural size; remainder approximately one-fourth natural size. Arrangement represents various morphologic changes (after Colbert).

early insectivores and are rather primitive. As is the case with most arboreal organisms, the geologic record of primates is poor. They apparently evolved from the tree-shrew and lemur groups. Higher types, including monkeys, apes, and man, probably had a common biologic ancestor during the late Cenozoic. Some students of primate evolution maintain that the record from the Pliocene to the Recent is rather complete for man's biologic evolution, and that "missing links" may no longer be stylish. Certain cave-dwelling types, dated at 500,000 years or so (*Australopithecus*), may be the link to the main line of primate ancestors and anatomical features of the numerous skeletons found apparently overlap with characteristics of the *Pithecanthropus* group. These later types, living 100,000 to 200,000 years before the Recent, gave rise to *Homo neanderthalensis*, which *must* have been the biologic ancestor of modern man, at least 50,000 years ago. Dimensions of cranial modification and teeth have played important roles in these determinations (Fig. 46).

The rates of evolution for man and his ancestors are high — much higher than the one species per million years which has been suggested as a reasonable rate for certain other mammals. The growth of the brain and the development of societies are only two of the many factors which are responsible for this unique event in mammalian evolution.

Glires

The rodents and rabbits may be grouped together in this category. If the ability to reproduce in great numbers is a valid criterion of success, then the real success story of mammals is from this group. Specialists have pointed out that there are more species of rodents than all other species of mammals combined. Large-sized populations have been an important factor in their success.

Earliest forms lived during the Eocene, and the small size of most representatives is such that numerous fossils have not been found. However, squirrels, rats, mice, gophers, beavers and porcupines are only a few of the rodent types which have been found in Cenozoic rocks (Fig. 47).

Modern beavers appeared in the Pleistocene, but their ancestors date from the Oligocene and include burrowing types. One of the most spectacular forms is a giant Pleistocene beaver, five feet or more in length.

Rabbits appeared early in the Cenozoic and have always been characterized by well-developed incisors, as is the case with rodents. These two groups give us an excellent example of adaptation; in this case adaptation to civilization.

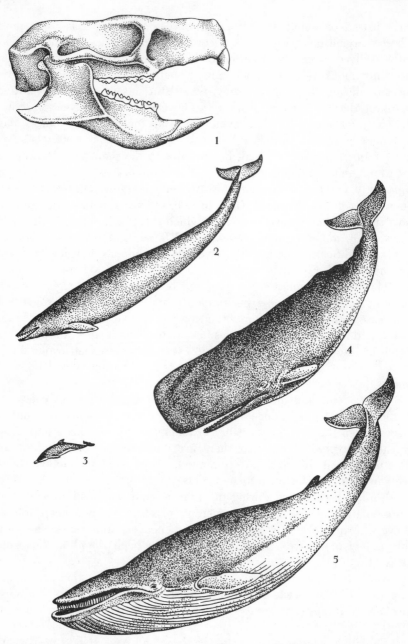

Figure 47. Rodents and whales. 1. an Eocene rodent, **Pseudosciurus,** approximately natural size (after Romer); 2. the Eocene ancestral whale, **Zeuglodon;** 3. a dolphin; 4. modern sperm whale; and 5. modern blue whale, all approximately one-twentieth natural size (after Colbert).

Mutica — (Cetaceans)

Certain early carnivorous mammals entered the aquatic environment in the Early Cenozoic and by the Eocene were quite well-adapted to marine life. This successful adaptation was accomplished relatively quickly and the development of the whales is such that the earliest fossil forms had already become excellently modified for swimming. Lungs are maintained and some forms can stay under water with a single breath for an hour. The entire group is quite intelligent and porpoises are often trained to perform a variety of stunts.

The trend toward giantism is especially well illustrated by whales. The large blue and green whales are the largest animals which have lived. Some are 100 feet or more in length, which is several feet longer than the greatest dinosaur and these types may weigh 150 tons — at least three times heavier than the greatest Mesozoic dinosaurs (Fig. 47).

Earliest Cenozoic varieties were more than 60 feet in length. Even though fossil whales are not common, sufficient material has been studied to show that the small and medium sized types, (porpoises, dolphins, killer whales, narwhals, etc.,) as well as the large toothless whalebone types, evolved from a common ancestor.

Ferrungulates

This large and diverse group includes the common hoofed forms of today, as well as a large number of distinctly different and extinct kinds. Included in this group are the even- and odd-toed mammals, (cattle, horses, and kin) the elephants, the carnivores, and certain marine forms such as the seals and walruses.

Extinct types include forms quite unlike any living today (Fig. 48). *Thomashuxleya*, an Eocene sheep-sized animal was an early member of one group whose descendants were the Pleistocene *Toxodon* (Fig. 48), a massive animal that stood six feet high at the shoulders and was a plant eater. Charles Darwin discovered the first specimen of this extinct species in South America. These ancient hoofed animals included a wide range of rodent to rhinoceros sized forms. One large group was restricted to South America and became extinct in the late Cenozoic.

Two of the most important hoofed types are the odd-toed (perissodactyl) and even-toed (artiodactyl) groups. These two groups evolved rapidly during the Cenozoic. The perissodactyls passed the height of their development and are almost an extinct group. The even-toed group are probably at the height of their development today.

The odd-toed group includes the extinct titanotheres and chalicotheres, the disappearing rhinoceros, and the horses and tapirs. Titanotheres were seven to eight foot animals with large horns and their chalicothere cousins were unique in possessing claws for digging. Tapirs of South America and Asia are living representatives of this primitive group. The rhinoceros and horse groups were much more diverse formerly and both seem headed toward extinction.

The evolution of the horse has been described for years as an almost ideal example of evolution. Views presented have sometimes oversimplified a very complex evolutionary history and it has been pointed out that the reduction in number of toes is only one factor drawn from many similar factors but from many different horse groups. Increase in size, complication of tooth structure, skull modification, etc.,

Figure 48. Ancient hoofed types. 1. **Thomashuxleya,** a five foot Eocene South American mammal; 2. **Toxodon,** Pleistocene rhinoceros sized mammal (after Colbert).

are a few of the important changes which affected various groups of horses during the last 60 million years (Fig. 49). All of these factors taken together from different groups must be understood for the real story of horse evolution.

The even-toed mammals are very successful hoofed types of the late Pleistocene and Recent. They are probably as widespread and numerous today as they have ever been. Pigs and hippopotamuses, camels and their kin, cud-chewing cattle, sheep, deer, etc., are only a few of the numerous kinds, living representatives of the mammals which are familiar to everyone. The camels first appeared during the

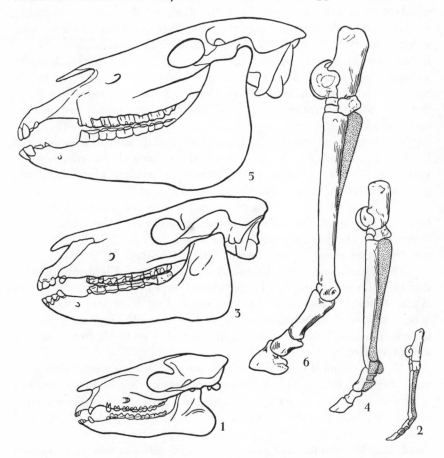

Figure 49. Stages in evolution of the horse. 1, 2. skull and hind foot of primitive horse, **Hyracotherium,** Eocene, approximately one-fourth natural size; 3, 4. skull of **Parahippus** and hind foot of **Merychippus,** Miocene, approximately 1/8 natural size; 5, 6. skull and hind foot of modern horse, **Equus,** approximately one-fourth natural size (after Colbert).

Early Cenozoic in North America and were fairly abundant in both North and South America until the Pleistocene when they migrated to the Eurasian area (Fig. 50). At that time, they became extinct in North America but are today represented in South America by the llamas. The llamas have continued with only modest change since the Miocene. In all groups there was a tendency to largeness expressed by long legs and long necks. Old World types were domesticated by early man. Immediate ancestors of the Old World camels evidently thrived in more northerly climates until just a few thousand years ago.

The meat eating mammals of the Cenozoic show excellent examples of adaption to a predatory mode of life. Their whole anatomy, including the jaw and tooth structure, illustrates complete adaption for carnivorous living (Fig. 51). Early forms showed some of these same features and during the Middle Cenozoic, the variety of minks, skunks, badgers, weasels, cats and dogs appeared and became well adapted to the ecologic niches which they occupy today. Some carnivores moved to the sea and the walrus, seal and sea lion are really just marine carnivores.

Excellent fossil carnivores have been found. Evolution was rapid in the group and few genera survived unchanged for many years. Differences between successive evolutionary stages are pronounced and data on evolutionary rates for the group are good.

Elephants have always been among the largest hoofed mammals. Little is known of the early evolutionary history of the group which appeared in the Eocene. Good specimens found in the Miocene show that the trend toward giantism was well established early.

The Pleistocene could be called the Age of the Elephants. During this time several varieties of now extinct types, spread over much of North America (Fig. 51). Their cousins, the mastodonts were also widely scattered in North America at this time. Evolutionary changes include a marked increase in length and size of tooth from early to Recent species.

Wooly mammoths and mastodonts were contemporaneous with early man (Fig. 51). Mastodonts were probably wandering in North America as recently as 8,000 years ago and legend says they may have existed until a few hundred years ago. In the Alaskan gold fields, thawing of frozen soils has revealed a great amount of skin, hair and bone of these animals. Whole specimens, meat and all, have been recovered from ice in Siberia.

Mastodonts and mammoths became extinct only a short time ago for reasons yet unknown and today only two species, the Indian and African elephants, remain.

Figure 50. Artiodactyls. The camels. 1. **Stenomylus,** small Miocene form approximately two feet high; and 2. **Alticamelus,** Pliocene camel, approximately 10 feet high (after Colbert).

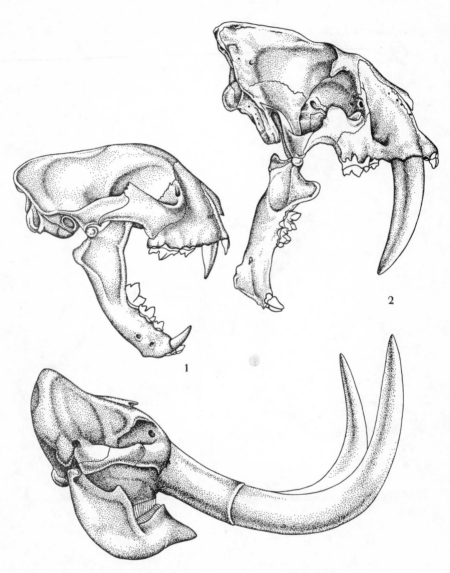

Figure 51. Carnivores and elephants. 1. A Pliocene cat, **Metailurus,** skull approximately six inches long; 2. **Smilodon,** the Pleistocene sabre tooth tiger, skull length approximately one foot; 3. **Mammuthus,** the wooly mammoth (X1/20) (after Romer).

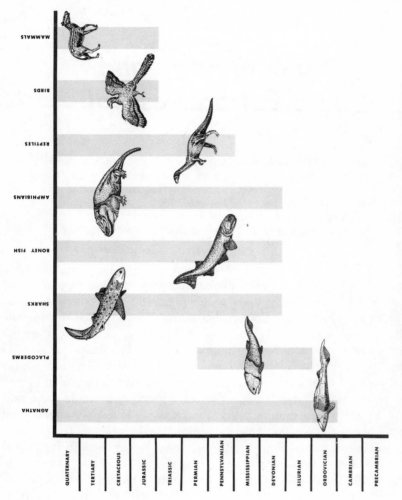

CHART 3. Development of the vertebrates and their distribution through time.

MAMMALS
BIRDS
REPTILES
AMPHIBIANS
BONEY FISH
SHARKS
PLACODERMS
AGNATHA

QUATERNARY
TERTIARY
CRETACEOUS
JURASSIC
TRIASSIC
PERMIAN
PENNSYLVANIAN
MISSISSIPPIAN
DEVONIAN
SILURIAN
ORDOVICIAN
CAMBRIAN
PRECAMBRIAN

CHAPTER

9

Paleontology and
Life Extraterrestrial

The probability of life extraterrestrially has led man to different
theories. While one theory is based on an idea of the existence of comparable or higher intelligence on other planets, the more biologically
oriented theories consider life elsewhere only possible but most likely
different from life on earth.

The study of paleontology tends to confirm these latter ideas.

Each form of life which has occupied space on our earth has been
unique. The Ordovician sponge-like animal with two walls separated by
pillars is unlike any living thing today (Fig. 18). A Cretaceous cephalopod with its large cane shaped shell (Fig. 27) as well as the Jurassic
reptile *Allosaurus* (Fig. 41), a fantastic reptilian carnivore, were all
unique, but representatives of "normal" life for the period of time in
which they lived. Today's spider monkey or the salmon would appear
equally curious to a Silurian age observer as past forms of life may
seem to us. And what is "normal" to our current view would seem odd
to the observer two million years from now. It follows, that the final
story of life of the earth will not be complete even when all the chapters
of paleontology are combined with the pages on our modern fauna and
flora. For living organisms continue to change, and the curious life
forms of the year 3,750,000 A.D. will constitute but another chapter in
the story of life. The life of any period of time of earth's history is
part of a continuously evolving lineage, and the most unusual form
of life is not really so unusual in relationship to the events and time
of its duration.

The time of a species' duration on earth is important for our understanding of life of the past, present and future. The particular environmental and genetical factors which are responsible for a certain form of

life do not remain long unchanged. The story of the earth is the story of change. On land and in the water, temperatures, food supplies, and all of the complex ecologic factors upon which life is dependent, are ephemeral. And it is a particular environment and a particular genetical system which interact to produce each form of life. The appearance of a certain type of organism during a specific period of geologic time was due to the fact that all of the internal and external factors which are collectively responsible, interacted in a particular way during that time interval. If any of these factors had been different, or had any worked together in a different way or at a different time, a different organism would probably have been produced. Thus, the giant among swimming reptiles, *Plesiosaurus* (Fig. 44), would not have been a *Plesiosaurus* under any other set of external and internal interactions except those which led to its development. Higher organisms have 100^{1000} possible number of gene combinations and the number of possible ecologic factors is also large. If these external and internal interactions are constantly changing, it appears unlikely that two species of the exact biologic make-up would ever develop, especially when separated by millions of years of change.

Herein is the explanation of each "unique" form of life. And herein too, rests the basis for speculation concerning life, extra-terrestrially.

Why speculation? In spite of all of the meteorites and their cargoes of "organic" material, none studied to date has been widely accepted as having been formed by life processes as we understand them. Currently, there is little direct evidence for life, except on this earth. However, it would be a sign of folly to maintain that there is no life extraterrestrially and the next meteorite may have definite organically formed matter. Further, the lack of positive evidence concerning the nature of life elsewhere, does not rule out the possibility of life other than on our earth. In fact, there seems to be widespread belief that there is much life elsewhere, and the evidence, although indirect, is the subject of much concern.

Although some of this concern is found on the comic page where Martian monsters with three eyes perform, more sober heads ponder the serious approach to this study. A unique environment and an event or events just statistically probable set in motion several billion years of evolution. The life produced by these unusual circumstances is everywhere around us and as part of it, we now can contemplate if, and how, a similar chain of events may have been set in motion elsewhere in our universe. While we give even the comics a Sunday morning scanning, the ideas now generated about life in our universe merit more than such a perfunctory glance.

We must admit, at first, that we know of no other planet where conditions just like those on earth have ever existed. Such ignorance does not rule out possibility, however.

There are apparently at least two opposite views on life extraterrestrial. The one maintains that there must be life present elsewhere and that this life may be at the same or at least in a similar stage of evolution as we believe ours is. Whether this is in our solar system or some other is not important. The other view is that because there is no evidence for life elsewhere, it is useless to speculate on its existence, and further, even if life does exist elsewhere in this or some other solar system, by its very nature, it would be considerably different from life on the earth.

There are various champions of these different views but, in general, non-biologically minded students maintain that intelligent, perhaps comparable, life exists elsewhere, while the more biologically minded students strongly maintain that if life does exist elsewhere, it would most likely be different.

These different ideas are based on different understanding (or lack of understanding) of the processes responsible for life. Life is being progressively reduced from a vitalistic to a chemical process. Life is literally in the hands of the chemist, the biochemist in particular, and while actions, reactions, and interactions of DNA, RNA, and other chemical structures may explain origin and physiology, the biologist who is concerned with the evolution and development of life apparently has greater insight into the nature of the kind of life which will ultimately appear.

The possibility that life elsewhere may be like that on earth is supported by several ideas. One is that life from earth may have been transported to other places in the solar system long before our first rockets performed this service. For instance, two of the principal theories for the origin of the moon support the idea that the moon was either derived from the earth initially or that it was derived from collision and then capture by the earth. In either of these theories, it could be supposed that the event occurred when there was some form of primitive life on the earth and that from either derivation, the moon and the accompanying fragments took some of this life with it. Because many of the meteorites with organic-like material may have ultimately been related to such an event it is also likely that other planets may have received transplants from mother earth in the same way. With such a common origin, why couldn't the product of evolution, several billions years later, be approximately the same?

An environmental approach has been used by yet other students of this problem. In this theory, the number of star-planetary systems possible in our universe is calculated. Further calculations of masses and other functions of these systems lead to the conclusion that there may be as many as four planets per visible star and that under the conditions of the calculations, around two planets per visible star may be in the "heat flux" zone, the space interval which could support life as we know it on earth. In our galaxy alone, some 10^{11} planetary systems may be available with potential earth-like environments. The conclusion is that "man is not alone . . .", his equivalent could be on hundreds or thousands of planets. It's a long way from the "heat flux" zone similarities to man's equivalent but a natural corollary to such an assumption is that forms of life equivalent to all earth's plants and animals may be abundant only a hop-skip and a light year away.

More biologically oriented students would take issue at this point. Although one may accept such calculations for the abundance of earth-like planets which *may* support life, our knowledge of the processes involved in evolution, at least on this planet, would suggest that any life present elsewhere, would, of necessity, be considerably different from that which has developed on earth. Given even the same physical and chemical factors in a gross sort of way and the same potential for development, there would still be variables of tremendous magnitude. The timing of the interactions of the varying micro-environmental factors would not be the same. There are many other unknowns. Under different gravity, magnetic, or other physical factors, how do chemical and biologic systems interact? Especially over a long period of time considerable differences in function and result are most possible. Our current space experiments may enlighten us here, but the long-term effects may only be apparent from long-term observation.

Because of the uniqueness of environment, genetics, and time, it appears unlikely that man's equivalents, at least in a recognizable form, could exist elsewhere, at least under the conditions proposed by the proponents of the theory.

Homeomorphs or very similar organisms, unrelated and separated by millions of years, do occur in the paleontologic record. These homeomorphs are never identical, however, and even when produced in strikingly similar environments there are differences of great magnitude.

Life extraterrestrially? The evidence indirectly from meteorites and theoretical calculations for environmental conditions in our galaxy seems to be positive. On the other hand, our understanding of the chemical and biologic factors of evolution suggests that whatever kind of life it may be, it would probably show considerable difference from that which exists today or has existed for several billion years on earth.

If our sun holds out, there may be another five billion years of evolution. Given this possibility, anything can happen.

Bibliography

Andrews, H. N., Jr., *Studies in Paleobotany.* New York: John Wiley and Sons, Inc., 1961.

Arkell, W. J., Furnish, W. M., Kummel, Bernhard, Miller, A. K., Moore, R. C., Schindewolf, O. H., Sylvester-Bradley, P. C., and Wright, C. W., Part L, Mollusca 4, Cephalopoda, Ammonoidea, in *Treatise on Invertebrate Paleontology,* R. C. Moore, (editor), Geological Society of America and University of Kansas Press, Lawrence, 1957.

Barghoorn, E. S., and Tyler, S. A., "Microorganisms from the Gunflint Chert," *Science,* v. 147, no. 3658, p. 563-577, 10 figs., 1965.

Bayer, F. M., Boschma, Hilbrand, Harrington, H. J., Hill, Dorothy, Hyman, L. H., Lecompte, Marius, Montanaro-Gallitelli, Eugenia, Moore, R. C., Stumm, E. C., and Wells, J. W., Part F, Coelenterata, in *Treatise on Invertebrate Paleontology,* R. C. Moore, (editor), Geological Society of America and University of Kansas Press, Lawrence, 1956.

Benson, R. H., Berdan, J. M., van der Bold, W. A., Hanai, Tetsuro, Hessland, Ivar, Howe, H. V., Kesling, R. V., Levinson, S. A., Reyment, R. A., Moore, R. C., Scott, H. W., Shaver, R. H., Sohn, I. G., Stover, L. E., Swain, F. M., Sylvester-Bradley, P. C., and Wainwright, John, Part Q, Arthropoda 3, Crustacea, Ostracoda, in *Treatise on Invertebrate Paleontology,* R. C. Moore, (editor), Geological Society of America and University of Kansas Press, Lawrence, 1961.

Bulman, O. M. B., Part V, Graptolithina, in *Treatise on Invertebrate Paleontology,* R. C. Moore, (editor), Geological Society of America and University of Kansas Press, Lawrence, 1955.

Campbell, A. S., and Moore, R. C., Part D, Protista 3, in *Treatise on Invertebrate Paleontology,* R. C. Moore, (editor), Geological Society of America and University of Kansas Press, Lawrence, 1954.

Cheetham, A. H., *Late Eocene Zoogeography of the Eastern Gulf Coast Region,* Geological Society of America Memoir 91, 1963.

Colbert, E. H., *Evolution of the Vertebrates,* New York: John Wiley and Sons, Inc., 1955.

Darrah, W. C., *Principles of Paleobotany,* 2nd. Ed., New York: The Ronald Press Co., 1960.

Easton, W. H., *Invertebrate Paleontology*, New York: Harper and Brothers, 1960.

Harrington, H. J., Henningsmoen, Gunnar, Howell, B. F., Jaanusson, Valdar, Lochman-Balk, Christina, Moore, R. C., Poulsen, Christian, Rasetti, Franco, Richter, Emma, Richter, Rudolf, Schmidt, Herta, Sdzuy, Klaus, Struve, Wolfgang, Størmer, Leif, Stubblefield, C. J., Tripp, Ronald, Weller, J. M., and Whittington, H. B., Part O, Arthropoda 1, in *Treatise on Invertebrate Paleontology*, R. C. Moore, (editor), Geological Society of America and University of Kansas Press, Lawrence, 1959.

Hass, W. H., Häntzschel, Walter, Fischer, D. W., Howell, B. F., Rhodes, F. H. T., Müller, K. J., and Moore, R. C., Part W, Miscellanea, in *Treatise on Invertebrate Paleontology*, R. C. Moore, (editor), Geological Society of America and University of Kansas Press, Lawrence, 1962.

Knight, J. B., Cox, L. R., Keen, A. M., Smith, A. G., Batten, R. L., Yochelson, E. L., Ludbrook, N. H., Robertson, Robert, Yonge, C. M., and Moore, R. C., Part I, Mollusca 1, in *Treatise on Invertebrate Paleontology*, R. C. Moore, (editor), Geological Society of America and University of Kansas Press, Lawrence, 1960.

Kulp, J. L., *The geological time scale*, International Geological Congress, Report of the Twenty-first Session, Norden, Part III, p. 18-27, 1960.

Moore, R. C., Lalicker, C. G., and Fischer, A. G., *Invertebrate Fossils*, New York: McGraw-Hill Book Co., 1952.

Muir-Wood, H., and Cooper, G. A., *Morphology, classification and life habits of the Productoidea (Brachiopoda)*, Geological Society of America Memoir 81, 1960.

Okulitch, V. J., and de Laubenfels, M. W., Part E, Archaeocyatha and Porifera, in *Treatise on Invertebrate Paleontology*, R. C. Moore, (editor), Geological Society of America and University of Kansas Press, Lawrence, 1955.

Olsson, R. K., "Foraminifera of latest Cretaceous and earliest Tertiary age in the New Jersey Coastal Plain": *Jour. Paleontology*, v. 34, p. 1-58, 1960.

Orbigny, Alcide d', *Paléontologie francaise; Terrains crétacés.* 1, Cephalopodes: Paris, A. Bertrand, V. Masson, 1840.

Romer, A. S., *Vertebrate Paleontology*, 2nd. Ed., Chicago: The University of Chicago Press, 1950.

Størmer, Leif, Petrunkevitch, Alexander, and Hedgpeth, J. W., Part P, Arthropoda 2, in *Treatise on Invertebrate Paleontology*, R. C. Moore, (editor), Geological Society of America and University of Kansas Press, Lawrence, 1955.

Stumm, E. C., *Silurian and Devonian corals of the Falls of the Ohio*, Geological Society of America Memoir 93, 1964.

Wodehouse, R. P., *Pollen Grains*, New York: McGraw-Hill Book Co., 1959.

Index

(Page numbers in boldface refer to illustrations.)

DATE DUE

MY 26 '72			
DE 19 '72			
AP 16 74			
MY 28 74			
OC _ 7 75			
OC 21 '75			
NO 25 '75			
NO 4 '80			
NO 8 '83			
MY 7 '85			
MY 21 '85			
MY 15 '90			
NO 13 '90			
MY 12 '91			
GAYLORD			PRINTED IN U.S.A.